The Last Years of British Railways Steam

The Last Years of British Railways Steam

Reflections, ten years after

O. S. Nock
B.Sc., C.Eng., F.I.C.E., F.I.Mech.E.

David & Charles
Newton Abbot London North Pomfret (Vt) Vancouver

British Library Cataloguing in Publication Data

Nock, Oswald Stevens
  The last years of British Railways steam.
  1. Locomotives—Great Britain—History
  I. Title
  385'.36'10941   TJ603.4.G7

  ISBN 0-7153-7583-0

Library of Congress Catalog Card Number
78–52158

Set and printed in Great Britain
by Latimer Trend & Company Ltd Plymouth
for David & Charles (Publishers) Limited
Brunel House Newton Abbot Devon

Published in the United States of America
by David & Charles Inc
North Pomfret Vermont 05053 USA

Published in Canada
by Douglas David & Charles Limited
1875 Welch Street North Vancouver BC

Contents

Preface

When David St John Thomas asked me to write a book about
the end of British steam, covering wide aspects of practice,
policy and performance, with—he added—some comment on
what might have been and what ought to have been, I hesitated.
The subject is so vast, so interlaced with cross-currents, political,
sociological, commercial, international, not to say emotional as
well. I had been in the thick of it myself in my daily professional
work, in my literary activities, and of course as a railway lover.
In thinking over the project memories came crowding in. As
an active member of the Institution of Locomotive Engineers I
was in touch with the leading personalities of the day, and the
informal talks before and after the set procedure of regular
meetings were illuminating. Then, of course, through my
literary work on locomotives I was in constant contact with
running superintendents, motive power inspectors, and others
on whom the heat and burden of the day inevitably rests, whatever views might be aired in more rarefied atmospheres. I re-
read some of my own comments printed at the time. Loughnan
Pendred, Editor of *The Engineer*, and his son Benjamin, who
succeeded him in the editorial chair, had insatiable appetites for
leading articles; and for a weekly journal they were needed
quickly. Very often, after a meeting in London, I would draft
the required leader on it in the train on the way home to Bath,

7

the same night. There was no time for reflection. But now, ten years after the last steam trains were run by British Railways, there *is* time for reflection, and provided one does not get immersed in a mass of detail the story of those last years can be woven into a co-ordinated narrative.

One could say that the end of British steam was foreshadowed even before World War II had ended; and the certainty of it came much nearer with the nationalisation of the railways in 1948. It is from this latter date that I have taken up the story; but I must emphasise that this is not a definitive history. It is more a survey of broad developments, conflicting trends, and the way the locomotive stock, and the train services fared in consequence. In reflecting upon the twenty years from nationalisation to the end of steam in BR-operated regular services, it could be terribly easy to be wise after the event, and to pontificate on what should, or should not have been done; but I have enjoyed the close personal friendship of many of the men who were most deeply involved, and I came to know their problems, and the appallingly conflicting influences from non-technical areas that often prevented the best technical opinion from being accepted in decision making.

Out of all the maelstrom that swirled around British Railways' headquarters in the *first* ten years of nationalisation, one point stands out crystal clear, and must be emphasised again and again. It is this: that however much the non-technical neophytes might chorus the utterly discredited shibboleth 'We shall be all right when we get rid of steam', it was the steam men who had to effect the transition—not the politician-salesmen, or the scrap-steam journalists! It was the dedicated railwaymen of all grades, with a lifetime of experience in steam behind them, who had to take the diesels and integrate them into the pattern of passenger and freight service; who, when their prudent technical advice on a three-year trial period was cast aside, and the lines began to be flooded with new power before the sheds and maintenance facilities were ready to deal with them, carried on, often

8

with hasty but necessary improvisations, and kept the traffic moving.

In 1975 my friend Roland Bond and I had the great honour of being invited to deliver the Clayton Lecture at the Institution of Mechanical Engineers, and in view of the sesquicentenary of the Stockton & Darlington Railway, our title was '150 Years of Uninterrupted Progress in Railway Engineering'. Bond was Chief Mechanical Engineer of the British Railways Board during the critical time of the transition from steam, and it is to his everlasting credit, and steam men like him, that progress *was* uninterrupted, and that so colossal a change in motive power was effected so smoothly, and in the face of appalling difficulties, so quickly.

Silver Cedars,   O. S. NOCK
High Bannerdown,
Batheaston, Bath   *October 1977*

1 Ten Years After

Ten years ago, on 3 August 1968 the last regular train service operated by British Railways with steam traction on standard gauge ceased. On that Saturday evening railway enthusiasts from all parts of Great Britain assembled at Preston to see, photograph, tape-record or travel on one or other of the two last trains—the 20.50 to Blackpool, or the 21.25 to Liverpool. It may have been a coincidence, but it was certainly appropriate that the last two steam trains for which intending passengers could just go to the booking office and buy a ticket were hauled by ex-LMS 'Black Five' 4-6-0s, surely one of the best general service machines in the whole history of railways. But though nostalgia was undoubtedly uppermost in the minds of the many who queued up for tickets that night, and who sang 'Auld Lang Syne' on the platform at Liverpool Exchange when one of those last trains came finally to rest, there was a significance infinitely beyond a change in the mode of traction. I take the liberty of quoting from some paragraphs I wrote in *The Railway Magazine* at the time:

We are nevertheless a little too near to events to appreciate to the full the profound significance of the epoch that has now ended. Many scribes have written nostalgically about the days of steam; albums of superb photographs have been published; and historians of all kinds—your humble servant among them—have been busy chronicling many diverse aspects of locomotive history. There is no doubt that the fascination of locomotive history will increase, as the steam era recedes further into history. Hardly a month passes without some diligent researcher turning up some 'find' in the way of a hitherto unknown document, and I have remarked before now on the frequency with which steam is still likely to form the centrepiece of discussion in these articles.

However, it is not detail, either in historical data or in actual running, that is uppermost in my own thoughts just at the moment. It is the immensity of the pageant that is now closed, and its worldwide implications. The steam locomotive, invented and developed in Great Britain, made world history on a colossal scale, not so much in speed records, power output and all the minutiae of detailed engineering, as in the advancement of civilisation in almost every continent the world over. In Africa, Australia, the Far East; in India, and South America, British engineers built railways for operation by steam locomotives, and it was the *British* steam locomotive, and its reliability in the superb quality of its workmanship and in its longevity that enabled pioneer railways in developing countries to be successfully operated.

In every country of the world the steam locomotive was the very cornerstone of the great sociological developments of the nineteenth century. A vast project like the Canadian Pacific Railway would never have been enterprised had there not been the certainty that once built there would be reliable power to work it. It was the same certainty of eventual sound operation when railroads were pushed westwards from Chicago, in the teeth of violent native opposition, or when the first railways were built in tropical Africa, and in the swamps and dense forests of countries like Burma. It is of course the British steam locomotive, above all others, that is foremost in our thoughts at the present time; and by British I mean not merely those that have worked on the home railways, but the products of the locomotive building industry. It is as well to ponder for a while on the extraordinarily wide ramifications of the great export trade in locomotives that was built up during the nineteenth century, and which reached its zenith in the years before the first world war.

Immensity of the pageant! The immensity of the way it ended was not the least part of the phenomenon. I am not now referring to that last night at Preston, nor of the crowds that gathered all along the linesides to see the farewell journey of Sunday, 11 August, from Liverpool, via Manchester, to Carlisle and back. It is just simple statistics that make one gasp! On New Year's Day 1955, when the modernisation plan was launched there were 18,426 steam locomotives in service on British Railways and in less than thirteen years they had all been withdrawn, scrapped, or otherwise taken out of revenue-earning service for BR. Eighteen thousand locomotives discarded in less than thirteen years. It was a fantastic operation. The total number of locomotives on the British main line railways had remained fairly constant over many years. At the close of 1938 for example it stood at 19,577; but the total number of withdrawals from the Big Four in 1938 was only 420, and against this 318 new locomotives were added. Thus at a time when great efforts were being made to work the traffic with fewer locomotives the total stock for the whole country was reduced by a mere 102. The average withdrawal rate from 1955 onwards was around 1400 per annum.

However much it dismayed lovers of the steam locomotive, and they included a very large number of professional railwaymen, the complete transition from steam in so short a time was a colossal feat of engineering and administrative planning. Some of it, from the outside, looked suspiciously like hasty extemporising, but by and large the travelling public suffered little or no inconvenience. In the period of extreme austerity since the end of World War II engine failures had become more frequent than previously known in Great Britain, and early troubles with the diesels were no more frequent than those currently occurring with steam. Whether the measures taken to effect the transition were the best, or the most economical will be debated as long as there are people interested in railways; but those responsible had a mandate imposed upon them in the most emphatic terms. Theirs was not to reason why, but to get the job done, and they did it extremely well. That much of it cut completely across the motive power policy developed in the first stages of nationalisation became evident as the startling details of modernisation took shape. That these were much more drastic than were at first conceived in the plan of 1955 was not to the liking of some of those responsible for the execution of the plan; but again it was done. How the diesels were introduced, and took over their duties is a later story, and it had some surprising and disquieting effects upon the motive power situation as a whole. Here I am concerned primarily with steam.

Of the 18,426 locomotives withdrawn between 1955 and 1968, many were fairly old. Some were very old. Many, on the other hand, were relatively new. Building of the British Standard classes had commenced in 1951, and continued at an average of 131 per annum until the end of 1957. After that construction of the splendid '9F' 2-10-0 heavy mixed-traffic type continued until 1960 to make that class the most numerous of all the BR Standards, with a total of 251. Except for the 9Fs, building of new steam locomotives ceased after the end of 1957 and the main-line diesels began to take the road in 1958. Why a further eighty of the 9Fs were built in 1958–60, in view of the rapid introduction of the diesels, is something of a mystery. Again, after the modernisation plan was launched in 1955 totals of 156, 129, and 141 locomotives of the standard classes, of power classes 2 to 5, and 9, were built in 1955, 1956 and 1957. Except for the 9Fs these were all of intermediate and low-power general service types, and it might have seemed more economical in overall policy to have withheld the withdrawal of older units over those three years, rather than build new ones for which the expectancy of life was not very long.

At that early stage in the working out of the modernisation plan, however, the advice of the technical branches of British Railways Headquarters was for a relatively gradual introduction of diesels, amounting to no more than 164 main line units, in four power ranges from 800 to 2000 horsepower. But this programme did not satisfy higher authority, and a policy of ruthless 'scrap and build' was launched. By the time the last steam locomotives had been taken out of traffic a total of 2872 main line diesels and 4000 diesel multiple-units had taken their place. The upshot of all this was that among the withdrawals were many medium powered standard locomotives little more than ten years old, while the newest of the 9Fs were barely eight years old. By automobile standards all these relatively new locomotives would be considered as life-expired; but if one looks at some of the regional classes that were being scrapped in the early 1960s, one can indeed rub one's eyes in perplexity. There were ex-Great Western 'Castles' more than 30 years old, still giving first class service, and Gresley non-streamlined Pacifics more than 40. There were small, but robust power units like ex-Caledonian Pickersgill 4-4-0s well over 40 years old, and Urie 4-6-0s on the Southern nearing the 45-year mark. With locomotives so substantially built as the new BR Standards a life-expectancy of at least 30 years would have been a reasonable prediction.

So, of course, it had been intended to be at the time the range of new designs was projected. The reason why the carefully thought out economic strategy was so summarily overthrown is discussed in later chapters of this book, and although it is rather like putting the finale before the overture, or before the denouement, one looks back somewhat wistfully to that epoch-marking Sunday of 11 August 1968, to the running of the last steam train, the special organised by British Railways, a week after the last ordinary steam passenger trains had run. It was a happy thought to include the magnificently scenic Settle & Carlisle line in the itinerary, and the clerk of the weather smiled graciously on the occasion. The engines concerned, the 'Black Fives' 44871 and 44781 might have been decked out for the royal train, rather than making their last bow in ordinary BR service, while the 'Britannia', No 70013 *Oliver Cromwell* looked superb.

It has seemed to need the signing of a death warrant, or the threat of one, to draw attention to some of the choicest parts of the British railway system, and its associated equipment. The Settle & Carlisle line is a case in point. Apart from a few rather amateurish shots published in the early days of *The Railway Magazine*, and a group of 'official' pictures taken near Armathwaite and little known until recent times, it was not until Bishop Treacy got to work in the 1950s that the scenic glories of the line were captured on film. F. E. Mackay never ventured further on to the line than Carlisle, and when my great friend and signal engineering colleague, R. J. Purves, got as far from North Eastern metals as to penetrate from Hawes to Hawes Junction, he secured no more than two shots, albeit in his own immaculate style. Admittedly in days before the ubiquitous private car choice photographic sites like the approach to Birkett Tunnel, Dent Head, Blea Moor or even Aisgill summit, were not easy of access by public transport, but then just look at the contrasting scene at Aisgill on 11 August 1968 when *Oliver Cromwell* paused there on the northward journey, and the spectators of both sexes of all ages could be counted in their hundreds, on the cutting sides, all over the tracks, sidings and main alike, with a solitary policeman standing in the cess on the up side to see fair play. The return train, hauled by the two 'Black Fives' made a water stop at Blea Moor.

The occasion was most vividly described in Roger A. Redfern's delightful book *Portrait of the Pennines*, thus:

'BRITANNIAS' AT WORK

Above: A Norwich–London express crosses Trowse Swing Bridge headed
by engine No 70001 *Lord Hurcomb* in July 1955 (*R. E. Vincent*)
Below: The Down Irish Mail passes Conway Castle; the engine is No 70050
Firth of Clyde and the date, 28 August 1964. (*Derek Cross*)

EX-LNER STANDARD TYPES

Above: Peppercorn Class 'A1' Pacific No 60149 *Amadis* on Newcastle express near Hadley Wood in 1954. (*E. D. Bruton*)

Below: Class 'B1' 4-6-0 No 61398 climbs Cockburnspath bank with an Edinburgh-Berwick stopping train in 1954. (*E. D. Bruton*)

This Midland Railway route, which became part of the LMSR in 1923, is full of character, and even today a journey behind a throbbing diesel locomotive is an exciting experience guaranteed to promote respect for the engineers who constructed the line between 1869 and 1876.

But perhaps the greatest single event for the Settle–Carlisle railway at least as regards the number of people gathered alongside the line throughout its entire length occurred on Sunday, 11th August 1968. This was the date decided by the British Railways Board on which all steam-hauled trains would cease to run, the end of the great era which really began on 15th September 1830, when the Liverpool–Manchester Railway was officially opened, a year after the famous steam locomotive trials at Rainhill between the two cities.

We were on that most scenic of all English railway routes where it climbs over and under the Pennines north of Ribblehead. The special train due to carry enthusiasts on the trip from Liverpool Lime Street to Carlisle and back called at Manchester and Burnley and was due to arrive at Ais Gill Summit at 1.45 p.m., where it would stop for twenty minutes for the passengers and the assembled lineside crowd to take photographs.

The morning dawned dry and warm, not a cloud in the sky, and when we arrived at Ais Gill many scores of cars were already parked. There was a holiday mood here and with two hours to go before the last remaining 'Britannia' (Pacific 4-6-2 type) No 70013 *Oliver Cromwell* was due to haul the special to a halt at this upland vantage point, many enthusiasts, young and old, were wandering over the main lines and examining the loop lines, cross-over and signal wire. This is the highest point on any British main line and the signal box here is normally one of the loneliest—today it was full to bursting with enthusiasts, police and railway officials!

Suddenly there was the distant whistle of a steam locomotive, and a pair of Stanier Class Fives came through running light, the engines which would be bringing the train back from Carlisle. They made a fitting introduction to the day's proceedings as they passed at speed.

The gangers came down the shallow cutting on to the track resplendent with orange pullovers, red and green flags, and a black horn apiece. Quite soon two police officers with a loud hailer announced the imminent passing of the south-bound 'Thames–Clyde' express and everyone was turned back behind the fence. As the last spectators retreated a ganger blew his horn three times, and the diesel-hauled train thundered through towards Settle and Leeds. The crowd increased and as zero hour approached we learnt that the train had just left Hellifield, where *Oliver Cromwell* had taken on water. It was already running late because of delay in getting sufficient water on board from the water column at Blackburn, which required the engine to be taken off the train and filled with 1,000 gallons from another column.

'It's just left Garsdale,' the policeman shouted to the crowd, and everyone pressed a little nearer to the fencing— Garsdale is only three miles away down the bank. Time passed slowly, and we imagined that the delay must be due to slow running past all the hundreds of enthusiasts lining the route between Garsdale, Shotlock Tunnel and Ais Gill. At last, it must have been a quarter-of-an-hour after the train left Garsdale, a ganger's horn blew, and the great bulk of the Pacific engine slid—slowly and almost silently—up to the summit and stopped opposite the signal box. The crowd swept down on to the line as one man and was joined by most of the 470 passengers. Still camera shutters clicked, cine-cameras whirred, and tape recorders were set in motion.

'Ais Gill has never seen anything like this before!' someone said as we crossed the main lines for the tenth time. I am sure they were right. The arrival of the first passenger train when the Settle–Carlisle route was opened on 1st May 1876 would not have seen a tenth of the crowd which brought the summit to life today. Because the train was thirty minutes behind schedule it only stopped for a quarter-of-an-hour. Then the guard's whistle blew, a loud hailer instructed the passengers to board the train immediately, and the locomotive's siren sounded. Jets of steam blasted along the track, and *Oliver Cromwell* moved off sedately, driving wheels spinning momentarily. Then the train was off, under the bridge and away down the upper Eden Valley. My last view of it was after a quick scramble to the nearby bridge parapet, where the already distant train was gathering speed, dominated by the great, shapely bulk of Wild Boar Fell. We would never again see such a plume of steam below that high Pennine hill as a train descended towards Carlisle.

We now drove the eleven miles southwards in order to see the train for the last time as it returned towards Liverpool. Perhaps the most scenically dramatic and beautiful stretch of the line is at Dent Head, where one can see the progress of a train as it comes southwards towards Blea Moor Tunnel's northern portal at Mossy Bottom. In the warm and sunny tranquillity of that August teatime we gathered on the cutting by the mouth of the usually dark and threatening tunnel. There was a feeling of mellowed melancholy, if there be quite such a thing. It was very hard to believe that it was almost all over, that never again should we see the spectacle of a British Railways' steam-hauled train. The bank on which we sat and chatted with fellow enthusiasts—there were only thirty or forty people about Mossy Bottom, in complete contrast to the hordes at Ais Gill—was pink with heather flowers, and across the line was a colony of rosebay willowherb in vivid bloom. We talked of 'Jubilees' which were no more—*Alberta, Straits Settlements* and the rest.

'She's coming, lads!' a man called from his wall-top perch, and there, sure enough, we could see the distant line of steam as the double-headed train sped around the 1,100 feet contour towards us. The sun gleamed upon Dent Fell and caught steam and paintwork in turn, then out of sight as it crossed Arten Gill Viaduct and entered the lengthy cutting protected by double rows of snow fencing. Again it came into view, passing the now-closed Dent Head signal box and sweeping over Dent Head Viaduct. The rapid beat of the shining Stanier Class Fives grew louder, and then they were passing and as quickly had gone with shrill whistles blowing—into the black depths of Blea Moor. The last blue and cream coach sped out of sight, and all that was left for us to see was the blue-grey smoke curling up from Mossy Bottom into the clear air. We ran at top speed up the 390 feet to the northern-most ventilation shaft in the hope of getting a photograph of the last smoke and steam issuing out over the moor, but virtually none came. However, this excursion had two rewards. Firstly, there was the wonderful vista of upper Dentdale and the fells in every direction, dappled with cloud shadows. There was no sound up there in the warm sunlight, though by going close to the smoke-blackened brick chimney at the top of the ventilation shaft the eerie trickle of drainage water down the 390 feet of railway level could be plainly heard. So we went down again to Mossy Bottom, and as we took a last look at the blue-grey smoke still curling out of the portal the second reward came. There was a sudden distant whistle, that of a steam locomotive! We could see another plume of steam as a light engine passed through Dent Station and came along the line towards Dent Head. It was *Oliver Cromwell* returning to Manchester—the very last British Railways steam locomotive to use this line. Out of the cutting over Dent Head Viaduct and on she came. There was little more than a whisper as the Pacific slid by, her green paintwork still shining the lowering western sun. A wave from the fireman, and she was gone at 30 miles an hour under Blea Moor; no whistle this time, just the gentle motion of the valves and a final curtain of blue-grey smoke at Mossy Bottom.

No more will steam traction raise the echoes romantically on the fells. I, for one, will always miss the fascination which this finest of all mechanical inventions has added to all types of country in general and to the Pennines in particular.

Could more be said!

I wrote the last sentence in 1977, but now, happily, more can *be said, because at the time of proof correction it has been announced that some steam specials are to be allowed over the line, and runs have already been programmed with the preserved ex-L.N.E.R. 'V2' 2–6–2 No 4771* Green Arrow.

2 Motive Power in 1948

The nationalisation of British railways, from the viewpoint of fixed equipment and rolling stock, could not have come at a more difficult time. The six years of war had left the whole system in a very run-down condition. Morale, where it had not deteriorated, was sadly disturbed, and then as if this had not been enough, there had come the terrible winter of 1946–7. This, added to the privation and austerity of the war years might, in other circumstances, have been the knock-out blow. It was however characteristic of the British people in general, and railwaymen in particular to rise above a seemingly catastrophic occasion; and with the Bill for railway nationalisation on the statute book all four of the main line companies spent the last months of their independence in some spirited enterprises that to the more dispirited of their admirers seemed to be no more than abortive swan songs. The appointments in the vital area of mechanical and electrical engineering did little to lift the gloom of the last months of 1947. Even though men of the former LMS had secured practically all the key positions in the new organisation, the company itself was dismaying the fans by inclining towards diesels.

R. A. Riddles, appointed member of the newly established Railway Executive responsible for mechanical and electrical engineering had an exceedingly difficult task ahead of him. The economic situation of the country was bad. After all the privations, distress, bereveaments and pure destruction of the war years, the actions of our former allies, both to west and east had forced upon us, on the one hand, severe austerity, and on the other a menacing international uncertainty and tension. Furthermore, few people were in the mood to appreciate, or even to try and appreciate, the tremendous service the railways had rendered during the war. If there were any thoughts, they would probably have been of their own discomforts and frustration in slow, unpunctual journeys in crowded, dirty, blacked-out carriages. I well remember how an acquaintance of mine responded, when I expressed concern at nationalisation. 'Well', he commented, 'the railways have made such a mess of it, I should think its about time someone else had a go.' In addition to a press and public that was generally unfriendly, the engineering staffs of the former group railways at first showed little inclination to shake down together under the banner of nationalisation.

Except for the LMS, which indirectly justified the choice of its men for the Railway Executive senior appointments, none of the mechanical engineering departments of the group railways was in a very healthy state. The Great Western was suffering from the effects of a prolongation under C. B. Collett of a policy of standardisation that had been overtaken by events. His successor, F. W. Hawksworth, was making the first steps towards modernisation by introducing a higher degree of superheating to combat the variation in steaming performance because of bad coal, but the isolation in which the Great Western had found itself after the unfortunate aftermath of the 1925 interchange trials persisted, and was accentuated by the antagonism shown towards the Institution of Locomotive Engineers by both Collett and Hawksworth—one of whom once referred to that distinguished body as a 'blue pencil lot of commercial travellers'! Hawksworth's only new design, the two-cylinder 4-6-0 'County' class, got off to a bad start, and the admirably conceived application of oil-firing on a limited scale came to nought following a colossal blunder by the Ministry of Fuel and Power. Above all, the top management of the former Great Western Railway had all too clearly shown its implacable opposition to nationalisation and all that it implied, and most of the senior officers who passed into the Western Region held much the same feelings. So far as Riddles was concerned therefore if help was to be forthcoming from Swindon, it had to be sought lower down the organisational tree.

On the Southern an extraordinary situation had developed, under the general managership of Sir Eustace Missenden. In the 1930s all available capital for new works had been devoted to the extension of the electrified system: after Brighton, to Eastbourne and Hastings, to Portsmouth, and then to the Medway towns as a preliminary to extensions to the Kent Coast. Under Sir Herbert Walker's direction steam traction became the Cinderella of the line. Then with the appointment of O. V. S. Bulleid to succeed Maunsell as chief mechanical engineer the Southern took into its fold a man who was an out-and-out steam devotee and who, remarkable to recall, had such advocacy as to persuade Missenden that there was a big future for steam on the Southern. It must have needed some extraordinarily eloquent talking to get authority to build such novel and complex machines as the 'Merchant Navy' class 4-6-2s in the middle of World War II; and then in 1945, to introduce the smaller 'West Country', with an eventual order for 110 units—yes 110 new medium power Pacifics! The fact that both 'Merchant Navy' and 'West Country' class were troublesome and relatively extravagant on coal and oil did not improve the situation, nor give Riddles much help in assessing his diverse inheritance.

Then, above all, the locomotive department of the LNER had been in a constant state of upheaval, ever since the death of Sir Nigel Gresley. His successor, Edward Thompson, had from sincerely held convictions begun to try and undo much that Gresley had achieved. But while his policy of introducing nought but two cylinder simple engines for medium power service, as the basis for a fleet of new standard engines had some justi- fication, his attack on the larger units, Pacifics, 2-8-2s and 2-6-2s aroused bitter resentment among the running staff who were intensely proud of all that had been achieved in pre-war years by 'A1', 'A3' and 'A4' Pacifics, and by the 2-8-2s in Scotland. As for the 'V2' 2-6-2s, the 'Green Arrows', one running super- intendent apostrophised them to me, in 1945, as 'the engines that won the war'. Thompson did not remain long, and when he was succeeded by A. H. Peppercorn, not long before nationalisation, the management of the locomotive department passed into the hands of a genial 'running' man, who of necessity had to leave matters of design in the hands of the pundits of the Doncaster drawing office.

On the LMS, in 1947, the house was happily in order, thanks to the wise administration of Sir William Stanier, who had not only managed his big department with technical skill and a warm human understanding, but had made wise provision for the future in the training of staff towards higher and middle- management. In consequence the LMS was able to furnish all the senior assistants that Riddles required, and still have adequate and experienced personnel to provide for the new London Midland Region. In 1947 it had been announced that on the LMS eleven locomotive types had been developed that could cover all requirements. Of these eight were well-established standards, as follows:

1. The 'Duchess' 4 cyl 4-6-2 express passenger.
2. The 'Converted Scot' 3 cyl 4-6-0 passenger.
3. The 'Black-Five' 4-6-0 mixed traffic.
4. The '8F' 2-8-0 freight engine.
5. The '4P' 2-6-4 passenger tank.
6. The class '3' 0-6-0 mixed traffic tank.
7. The class '2' outside-cylinder 0-6-0 tank.
8. The 0-6-0 diesel shunter.

Three further standard classes were introduced in 1947, two of Class '2' capacity, namely the 2-6-0 tender engine and the 2-6-2 light passenger tank. The last was the Class '4' 2-6-0, which did not appear until just before nationalisation.

Thompson had propounded a scheme of standardisation for the LNER not long after he had succeeded Gresley, including 4-6-2, 4-6-0, 2-8-0, 2-6-0, 2-6-4T and 0-6-0 tender engines, but at the time of nationalisation the 4-6-2 was not yet a proved design and the 0-6-0 was merely a modernisation of an early Great Central design. Riddles and his staff had a clear mandate to standardise motive power over the whole country, and the possibilities before them were unlimited. At the outset they took a step that simultaneously galvanised interest, enthusiasm, partisanship, and which was of priceless psychological value in bringing together in a common project the locomotive engineering staffs of all four group railways; this was the announcement of the locomotive interchange trials that were to begin within five months of vesting date. The former chief mechanical engineers whose status had been much reduced were not more than mildly interested, particularly as admission to the dynamometer cars was under close scrutiny and censorship; but their seconds in command, and their immediate assistants were thrown into the thick of it, and immediately had to work with each other on a common project.

This was undoubtedly the greatest asset of the whole project, because as comparative tests of locomotives the results were completely inconclusive in all the three groups of trials. With a certain amount of hindsight they have been criticised by certain people as a great waste of money—public money now that the railways were nationalised; but such criticism is to miss completely the very considerable gains that were achieved in bringing the locomotive engineers of the nationalised railways a little nearer to becoming a unified team. It is interesting to look back to that January of 1948 and try to discern what was hoped for as a result of such a large scale interchange of locomotives. The overriding aim was never in doubt: to settle upon a range of standards that would provide adequate and efficient motive power for the entire British Railways system, in the foreseeable future. The first question one would ask, however, in 1948, was, 'Why steam?' Within a year the last main line steam locomotives would have been built for service in the USA. Were not British Railways dropping behind, when this opportunity to modernise was offered?

In asking these rhetorical questions I must refer back to the economic state of the country as a whole. Diesel locomotives need oil, and oil had to be imported. We had not then sufficient foreign exchange to buy the oil, and a second consideration was that the cost of diesel-electric locomotives was then roughly two and a half times that of a steam locomotive of equivalent tractive power. Furthermore, if an immediate switch to diesel traction had been decided, it is more than a little doubtful if British industry would have been able to supply the new locomotives in the quantities required. Be that as it may, Riddles expressed his chosen policy in very simple terms: 'We are going to have the form of motive power that gives the most tractive effort *per pound sterling*.' That of course was steam.

Quite apart from any conclusions that might be drawn from the Interchange Trials the matter of replacement of ageing and obsolete units had to go on. All former independent railways had placed orders on their various works for 1948, and these were allowed to continue, pending decisions by the Railway Executive as to how their mandate for standardisation should be implemented. The following record of new construction during 1948 shows clearly the lines that were followed by the former independent companies:

ex-GWR: 10 'Castles';
              15 'Halls';
              2 0-6-0s '32XX' class;
              10 2-6-2 passenger tanks '41XX' class;
              27 0-6-0 tanks.

ex-Southern:	8 'Merchant Navy' 4-6-2s;
	19 'Battle of Britain' 4-6-2s.
ex-LMS:	1 Pacific (No 46257);
	40 'Black Five' 4-6-0s;
	20 Class '4' 2-6-0s;
	15 Class '2' 2-6-0s;
	46 Class '4' 2-6-4 tanks;
	20 Class '2' 2-6-2 tanks.
ex-LNER:	21 Class 'A1' Pacifics;
	14 Class 'A2' Pacifics;
	46 Class 'B1' 4-6-0s;
	60 Class 'L1' 2-6-4 tanks.

It may also be recorded that the total number of steam locomotives that came into British Railways ownership on 1 January 1948 was 20,024. This had been reduced to 19,659 by the end of the year.

Among the standard locomotives being perpetuated the ex-GWR 'Castles' and 'Halls' were of the Hawksworth variety, with higher degree of superheat. The ex-LMS 'Black Five' 4-6-0s included a batch with Caprotti valve gear, while the Class '4' 2-6-0s were of the new design prepared under H. G. Ivatt's direction and mentioned earlier. The LNER 'B1' and 'L1' classes were of Thompson design. Although not included among new locomotives it should be added that the LMS programme had included the systematic replacement of the original 'Royal Scot' 4-6-0s by the taper-boilered 'Converted' variety, of which four such transformations were made in 1948. Up to the end of 1947 a total of 42 out of 70 locomotives had been so treated, and the process went on after 1948 until the whole class had been converted by the end of 1955. At the same time work had commenced with renewal of the 'Baby Scot' class, with the same '2A' boiler and improved front end. Eight of the class had already been treated by the beginning of 1948, and another nine were converted during the year; but after only one more had been similarly rebuilt in 1949 this programme was not continued.

The most controversial among the new locomotive construction programmes of 1948 and 1949, allowed to continue by the Railway Executive, were the Pacifics of former Southern and LNER design. Another two 'Merchant Navy' class, and eleven 'Battle of Britain' 4-6-2s were added in 1949, together with 28 Class 'A1' 4-6-2s of Peppercorn design for the former LNER lines. There were times indeed when the operating departments seemed in difficulty as to how to use so many of these large engines, and they were often seen to be very lightly loaded. Neither could any of these Pacific engines be regarded as entirely successful, either mechanically or thermodynamically. Much has been written of the vagaries of the Bulleid Pacifics to which it would be inappropriate to add anything more here; but of the Peppercorn Pacifics one or two comments may be added. That they were very strong and free running engines will not be disputed, but as originally designed they had some disturbing characteristics in their riding, due to inadequate side control on their leading bogies. What revealed them most unfavourably beside the Gresley Pacifics however was their appetite for coal.

Again with hindsight, the use of a firegrate as large as 50sq ft would now seem to have been an error of judgment. It arose in the first place from Edward Thompson's drastic rebuilding of the Gresley 'P2' 2-8-2s, as Pacifics. Those engines had been designed for very heavy intermittent work on the Edinburgh–Aberdeen route, and the same boiler was used on the subsequent Thompson and Peppercorn 4-6-2s. But while it is an excellent thing to have ample steaming capacity, too large a grate can be a liability when a locomotive is being worked at less than optimum capacity, when coal has to be fired simply to keep the bars covered. A running superintendent with lifelong experience of the East Coast Route once made to me this distinction between the Gresley and Peppercorn Pacifics: 'The Gresleys are the greyhounds of the service, but if you have to take 600 tons on a dirty night, give me a Peppercorn every time.' With his running experience of the war years, when the East Coast was habitually

31

taking loads of 600 to 700 tons, Peppercorn had good reason to specify 50sq ft grates for his new Pacifics. The only trouble was that by 1948 the 600 ton passenger trains no longer existed.

When the Interchange Trials of 1948 were first projected, it was originally hoped that in the heavy express passenger class the Eastern Region would be represented by a Peppercorn 'A1'; but the first of these engines had not been long enough in traffic for Doncaster to be sure of its behaviour, and the choice then fell back upon the Gresley 'A4'. In the event, no fully comprehensive or quantitative analysis of the performance of the Peppercorn Pacifics, either of the 'A1' or 'A2' classes was ever made, though both classes established an excellent record of immunity from failure, and of relatively low cost in running repairs. Nevertheless, among all grades in the running departments of the Eastern, North Eastern, and Scottish Regions there were 'Gresley' and 'Post-Gresley' factions. Among the many different engine designs for which Riddles assumed responsibility in 1948, one rather stood out from the rest—the Gresley 'V2' 2-6-2. There was nothing quite like it on any of the other railways, for although the Bulleid lightweight Pacific of the Southern was in much the same power classification, it had been designed primarily as an express engine. The 'V2' on the other hand was intended as a fast, heavy freighter, to handle the long distance fitted goods traffic that the LNER management was so assiduously developing before World War II. The fact that the 'V2s' proved such versatile engines as to be used in really fast passenger service was at first pleasing, but incidental. During the Thompson regime on the LNER, and for a little time afterwards the reputation of the 'V2s' was apt to be discredited by the anti-Gresley faction, because of failures of the conjugated valve gear on the inside cylinder, but to those who really knew their worth they will always be remembered as great engines. As will be shown later, their existence in some strength and the class of duty for which they were designed had its influence on future British Railways' practice.

3 Standardisation—the choices before Riddles

The events of 1948 left the mechanical and electrical engineers' department of the Railway Executive with a variety of problems to resolve. As an ex-LMS man, and with his two principal assistants of the same ilk, he undoubtedly felt, 'deep down inside', that the LMS engine designs were the best, and there can be little doubt that every one concerned in former years with the LMS hoped that the interchange trials would show this superiority in so convincing a way that adoption of the existing LMS standards would be a foregone conclusion. After all, the LMS had, readymade as it were, a range of locomotives that was sufficient to cover the needs of the entire system; and there were no sections of any of the former independent railways that had physical characteristics or traffic demands more diverse than those of the LMS, extending from Bournemouth and Shoeburyness to Wick and Thurso; from Swansea to Hull and York. The possible exception was on the East Coast main line north of Edinburgh; but there, as on the Highland line, the LMS would have been prepared to double head, if necessary.

Unfortunately the interchange trials did not happen that way. The very nature of the project left immense scope—or perhaps I ought to say loopholes!—for the intrusion of personalities. To secure the absolute fairness in approaching the whole exercise that Riddles and his men so desired, it was decreed that apart from road pilotmen, and a relatively junior observer from the dynamometer car staff of the testing Region, the drivers and firemen should be left on their own during the test runs. Locomotive running inspectors travelled on the trains, and were at liberty to instigate or caution before and after; but they were not able to give any guidance while on the run. How the individual engine crews were chosen I do not know, but taken all round the ex-LMS locomotives were not too happily served. One of the great surprises and disappointments of the whole affair was the very poor showing made by the Stanier 'Black Five' 4-6-os—so completely unrepresentative of their normal performance. To all outward appearances their work was definitely outshadowed by that of the Thompson 'B1' 4-6-os from the ex-LNER areas. Again, in the mixed traffic engine category the work of the ex-GWR 'Halls' was disappointing, largely because of circumstances connected with their manning.

Any chance of Great Western locomotives being adopted as future standards was virtually ruled out before even the trials started by their restricted route availability, which precluded their running over any parts of the former LMS and Southern lines. The essential difference between a 'Hall' and a 'Black Five', which might have been brought out more clearly had the former type been permitted to run over the Highland line, lay in the valve gear. It was of no small interest to those who appreciate the special characteristics of the Stephenson's link motion that the LMS had built experimentally one engine in the 'Black Five' series, No 4467, with the link motion, arranged outside, and that it had proved remarkably successful. However the 'Hall' was given little opportunity to show its ability to climb heavy gradients.

A lasting memory of those who had any personal contact with the interchange trials was of the highly spectacular performance of the Bulleid 'West Country' Pacifics, which were driven and fired with tremendous verve and enthusiasm, and, be it added, at times with little regard for coal consumption or for schedule

EX-LMS STANDARD TYPES

Above: Stanier Pacific No 46245 *City of London* with a special headboard
for Coronation year in 1953. (*British Railways*)
Below: LMS three-cylinder 4-6-0 No 45552 *Silver Jubilee* on up express
leaving Primrose Hill Tunnel. (*British Railways*)

THE GRESLEY V2s ABROAD

Above: Engine No 60845 on dynamometer car trials near Hullavington, during re-draughting tests at Swindon. (*K. H. Leech*)

Below: Engine No 60893, on loan to the Southern Region in 1953, during the temporary withdrawal of 'Merchant Navy' class 4-6-2s, here seen on the Bournemouth Belle near Basingstoke. (*M. W. Earley*)

times! I learned some time afterwards that they had an unofficial mandate from their shed master to 'go and lick the pants off everybody else'. They certainly did, so far as running times were concerned. It may have confused the issue, but it delighted the enthusiasts. To what extent such performances influenced the forward thinking of the Railway Executive it is difficult to imagine. Bulleid, like the other regional chief mechanical engineers, found he had to obtain permission to ride in the dynamometer cars on the test runs, and did not find restrictions of that kind much to his liking; but despite his strongly individualistic outlook, and his disagreement with much of the new policies being evolved, he could not be accused of 'rocking the boat'.

Had the Railway Executive had to depend entirely upon the results of the interchange trials for the substance on which to base their future policy, they would indeed have been in the throes of a dilemma for all time. In the express passenger group the Gresley 'A4' Pacifics came out on top so far as coal consumption was concerned, but earned some black marks from failures of the conjugated valve gear. That the incidence of failure in relation to mileage run was wildly out of keeping with the standards of performance for the class in ordinary service on its own line was appreciated, but as explained earlier the Gresley 'A4' was not the Eastern Region's first choice for the job. The 'Duchess' and the 'Scot', representatives of the LMS standard range, showed no superiority over the others that would justify their adoption as future standards. The 'King' and the 'Merchant Navy' were out on other considerations.

Against the results of the trials, which had given such contradictory and inconclusive evidence of achievement, the ex-LMS men at the Railway Executive had the solid, fully authoritative bank of data which had been collected on the LMS since the late Lord Stamp had initiated the system of individual costing of every locomotive on the line. Against this constantly critical scrutiny of performance the Stanier locomotive stud had been

C 37

developed and improved, and there must have been a great temptation to adopt the standard range that they knew intimately, and which had a very completely documented record of performance in all its widest and most far-reaching aspects. But they realised that to announce such a decision would cause the strongest resentment among men of the other Regions, particularly on the Western. Furthermore there was another factor that came to influence future policy, and that was the type of power needed for immediate traffic requirements. If the ex-LMS standard range had been adopted, would the two largest units—the 'Duchess' 4-6-2 and the 'Scot'—4-6-0 meet the immediate needs of British Railways?

Another course would have been to share the honours out, taking existing, well-proved designs in the express passenger, mixed traffic, freight and suburban tank classes, one from each of the Regions. But apart from the difficulty there would have been in finding any Great Western design in any of the four categories that would be acceptable to the other Regions on the grounds of route availability alone, such a course would have cut completely across the policy of standardisation. Instead of the Regions having only their pre-nationalisation standards to deal with—albeit differing from Region to Region—they would each have had to assimilate three more alien practices. Such a course, though savouring of impartiality, would have been thoroughly impracticable.

The third course, and by far the most difficult and expensive, would be to evolve an entirely new national standard that would incorporate all that was best in the existing Regional practices, and apply this to such new locomotives as were required in replacement of time-expired and obsolete classes in the Regions. This, as is well known, is the course that Riddles adopted. It can be seen now as an heroic gesture—the inception of a philosophy based upon an ideal, that it was hoped would eventually please everybody, and go a big step further forward in uniting the greatly dissimilar Regional practices and outlooks in a common aim. Even at the time, however, there were many, both inside the railway service and outside, who questioned its wisdom. I shall never forget being told by one of my friends at Paddington how horrified Sir Felix Pole had been at the capital charges associated with the introduction of a new locomotive design, in the particular case, the 'King'. It was not the simple ironmongery involved in construction, but all the planning, new patterns, tooling and workshop machinery that was involved, even before the moulders could get to work or the first frameplates could be cut. It would be the same many times over with a complete new range of standard locomotives, especially as in pursuing the principle of impartiality the work would need to be distributed between the manufactories of the former group railways.

Then, in studying the existing locomotive stocks and the ranges of standard types that had been evolved on the former GWR, Southern, LMS and LNER, the question arose as to what new designs should first be produced. In this the traffic conditions prevailing at the time provided a most important consideration. Austerity still had the country in its grip in 1949. The ravages of wartime service, accentuated by the winter of 1946-7, had affected tracks to an almost unbelievable extent, and the frequency of speed restrictions due to track repairs, or over sections that were awaiting them, had been a marked feature of the running on many routes during the interchange trials of 1948. In consequence a return to the standards of express train running prevalent in 1938-9 was remote. Locomotives of tractive power less than the maxima on some routes could deal adequately with the traffic, while on others the lavish provision of Pacific locomotives of maximum power, since the war, had stopped somewhat ahead of actual requirements. From these two causes, on British Railways as a whole, there was little if any need for new express passenger locomotives in the immediate future. Thus the Railway Executive was spared the terrifying task of producing a new design that would be a synthesis of all the best features of a 'King', a 'Duchess', Peppercorn 'A1', or a

'Merchant Navy'! Passing a little further down the power scale, the 'Castle', the 'Converted Scot' and the 'Lord Nelson' were more closely related, but again the need for such a new type was not uppermost.

The next step down, in the standard ranges of all four of the former companies, was to the mixed traffic 4-6-os, 'S15', 'Hall', Black Five, and 'B1'; orders for the last three of these classes were then in hand. But the first new standard class under the British Railways' flag had essentially to be a symbol; a peg round which publicity for the new era could be built up, and which would display in its outward and mechanical appearance not only a new look that was to be characteristic of the new range, but which would display to discerning onlookers the extent to which features of earlier practice of all four of the old companies had been blended. Obviously it could not be one of the medium powered mixed traffic classes. It had got to be a big engine. The former LNER had demonstrated the outstanding value of a large mixed traffic class, in the Gresley 'V2' 2-6-2, and with the prospect of long distance fast fully-fitted freight services being developed, a large mixed-traffic design would be an impressive and appropriate beginning for the new standard range. Furthermore, experience with existing designs on the LMS and LNER had shown that coupled wheels of around 6ft 0in diameter were no handicap to the attainment of maximum speeds up to 90mph, so that a large mixed traffic engine could be used, in passenger service if necessary, as the Gresley 'V2s' had been before World War II.

The choice of the Pacific wheel arrangement was a little open to question. Casting the nets world wide, one of the most outstandingly successful locomotive designs of recent times had been the Chapelon rebuild of the original Orleans small-wheeled Pacific of 1907 as a 4-8-0, and in view of the remarkable work performed on occasions during the 1948 interchange trials by the 'Converted Royal Scots' a 4-8-0 development on the same lines, with smaller coupled wheels might have seemed a possible development. All British Pacific designs then in service seemed prone to slipping to a far greater extent than 4-6-os—some, at times, to a most embarrassing extent, and in a mixed traffic unit from which rapid acceleration, and an ability to climb steep gradients were essential requirements, a propensity to slip was clearly undesirable.

There was also of course the question of the boiler. In respect, particularly of the Chapelon 4-8-os, while French locomotives generally used poorer grades of coal than were normal, even in the post-war years of austerity, on British Railways, the degree of specialisation among French enginemen with a limited number of specific units was far greater than in Great Britain, and no difficulty was experienced in securing a high rate of evaporation in a long, deep, narrow firebox. Any new British locomotives in the standard range would, on the other hand, require to be easily manageable by all and every crew, on any of the varieties of coal supplied in different parts of the country. Much study had been made of current American practice, even though most of those railways were then rapidly changing over to diesel traction, and the consensus of opinion was that for a large new mixed traffic locomotive a wide firebox with large grate area was essential. This seemed to rule out the 4-8-o, and made the Pacific type inevitable.

Apart from this one innovation of a mixed traffic Pacific, which could also undertake express passenger duties of a category already being worked by 'Castles', 'Royal Scots', and 'Lord Nelsons', and of course the light-weight Bulleid Pacifics of the 'West Country' and 'Battle of Britain' classes, the rest of the first group of standards announced looked like thinly disguised perpetuations of existing LMS standards. In so saying, however, it must be confessed that the three new LMS standard classes introduced after the war were not entirely satisfactory in their respective original forms. These were the Class '4' 2-6-o, numbered from 3000 upwards, the Class '2' 2-6-o, and the corresponding Class '2' 2-6-2 tank. The two last mentioned were intended for light branch and short distance local work; although originally designed to meet purely LMS requirements, and introduced before nationalisation, after 1948, some of these 2-6-0 tender engines were drafted to other areas where existing locomotives were reaching the end of their economic lives, or were thought to be so. A particular instance, which had some rather startling repercussions, occurred on certain branch lines of the former GWR in Central Wales.

In the event, it may seem strange that with the magnificent record of the Stanier regime behind it the LMS should in its last years have produced three new designs that did not come up to expectations, and all in the same vital respect—a limited capacity for raising steam. The Class '4' 2-6-0, despite the outward signs of ultra-modernity in the form of twin orifice blastpipe and double chimney, high raised running plate to give maximum accessibility, and an apparently well designed firebox, just would not steam, of which failing I had some soul-destroying footplate experiences on the Somerset and Dorset line. The Class '2' 2-6-0s steamed satisfactorily up to a point, but when they were put on to certain heavily graded lines in Central Wales in replacement for the veteran Dean goods 0-6-0s of the GWR, to the consternation of all concerned, and to the delight of pro-GWR partisans, the new 2-6-0s were found incapable of equalling the performance of the veterans.

A good deal about smokebox draughting was learnt from the early behaviour of those new standard 2-6-0s of the former LMS, and the experience proved invaluable when the new British Railways standard designs were developed from those earlier LMS essays. From 1948 onwards the staff of the mechanical and electrical engineers' department, at headquarters and at all the regional centres, was involved in an urgent and highly complex endeavour to produce the new standard range; but viewing it all in retrospect one must be pardoned for asking if it was really worth while. There is no doubt that Riddles and his men envisaged a much longer tenure of life for the steam locomotive in Great Britain than actually eventuated. The point is, could not its demise have been more clearly foreseen, at the time they embarked upon the programme of locomotive standardisation. Is it safe to suggest that if, in 1949, it had been anticipated that around 1955 the modernisation plan would be launched, with the complete elimination of steam traction as one of its major points, would the production of the standard locomotive range ever have been started? It is a searching, if hypothetical question. Riddles himself was firmly opposed to the introduction of diesel traction, and considered that all funds available for the modernisation of the traction system should be devoted to main line electrification, leaving steam to carry on elsewhere.

4 The BR Standard locomotives and their impact

With some skill in timing, and perhaps a little luck, the first new standard locomotives took the road early in 1951, a year in which the country was at least beginning to climb out of the slough of postwar austerity. It was a situation signalled by the Festival of Britain, and some welcome publicity by British Railways. The new Pacifics, beginning with the symbolically named No 70000 *Britannia*, came into power class 7, thus joining the second line express passenger types, such as the 'Castles', 'Converted Scots' and 'Lord Nelsons', but with the suffix 'MT' rather than the 'P' of the express engines just mentioned. But although the new locomotives were designated 'mixed traffic' all were named. A batch of 25 was built at Crewe in 1951, and they were distributed between the Great Eastern Line of the Eastern Region, the Southern, and the Western Region. Engine No 70004 *William Shakespeare* was given an exhibition finish, and displayed at Battersea during the Festival of Britain exhibition during the summer of 1951, while the ten allocated to the Western Region, Nos 70015–24 were given the names of famous broad gauge engines. There was however a joke going the rounds in 1951, that a certain gentleman with the homely accent of Cockaigne thought that No 70017 *Arrow*, belonged to the 'Schools' class!

The 'Britannias' had a somewhat mixed reception. On the Great Eastern Line they were by far the most powerful locomotives yet to be introduced in that area, and their enhanced power, and high steam raising capacity made them generally welcome. Once the running staff had taken the measure of the new engines a notable acceleration of service was made possible. They were used primarily in express passenger work, but the diagrams were arranged to include certain fast freight, and taken all round a high degree of utilisation was obtained from them. The train timing enthusiasts enjoyed the fast running, and noted particularly the high speed maintained uphill. On the Southern one or two of them were tried experimentally on Waterloo–Bournemouth trains, but a more permanent usage began on the Continental boat expresses from Victoria, on which they took turns with the 'Merchant Navy' class Pacifics. Following the exhibition period at Battersea, No 70004 *William Shakespeare* was put on to the Golden Arrow service—always something of a prestige job.

The ten locomotives allocated to the Western Region were divided between Old Oak Common and Laira sheds, and, being so different from any Great Western designs, were received with caution. The running inspectors studied them carefully, and loyally strove to make good use of them, but many of the enginemen were not so co-operative. They could not understand why a much larger, clumsy, and noisier engine was needed to do what they had for so many years done satisfactorily with 'Castles'. They found them very dirty engines on which to work, though at the other end of the scale there were a few drivers who voted them the best they had ever had, better even than a 'King'. This small minority certainly included one very senior driver who was entrusted with many special workings. The London engines worked to Bristol, and on the second grade West of England duties, while the Plymouth engines worked to Bristol, and on the Cornish main line. My own first experiences of them in the Western Region were actually better than those on the Southern, and in East Anglia, but in this I think I was fortunate in the crews with whom I travelled. I had a particularly good run with engine No 70019 *Lightning* from Penzance to Plymouth on the up Cornish Riviera Express. These runs were made in the late summer of 1951, and gave the general impression that the engines had made a successful debut. What I did not know, at the time of making them, was that a curious and potentially serious trait had begun to show.

In July 1951, engine No 70014 *Iron Duke*, in service on the Southern Region, failed with all its coupled wheels coming loose on their axles. This was alarming enough, but reports of six other cases came in shortly afterwards. Repairs were effected, and the remaining eighteen engines of the first batch continued in service. It was indeed in this very period that I made my own first footplate trips. Then, in October 1951, while working the up Golden Arrow and running at high speed near Headcorn, No 70004 *William Shakespeare* began slipping; all the coupled wheels shifted on their axles, and one of the side rods was fractured. After the earlier, but less serious troubles of the same kind, the risk of this could not be allowed to continue, and Riddles withdrew all engines of the class from service, pending investigations. When the news leaked around there was unholy joy among the anti-nationalisation partisans, and caustic comments that after all this time one would have thought there would be means to prevent wheels falling off! The very urgent technical investigation revealed certain detailed weaknesses in the method of mounting the wheels on the axles which gave rise to the shifting only when the manufacturing tolerances on all the mating parts were one way. That accounted for the phenomenon that while wheels shifted on the axles of some engines of the class, but remained perfect, without a sign of trouble on others—some of which latter had been subjected to exceptionally heavy usage. Swift measures were taken to correct the trouble, and very soon all the engines of the class were back to give a service that was troublefree thenceforward.

It was perhaps at Norwich that the merits of the 'Britannias' were most enthusiastically acclaimed. Eight engines of the class were stationed there, and they did an immense amount of hard and fast running. It was the early prowess of those engines that gave the operating department confidence to accelerate the fastest trains from London to a run in the even two hours, for 115 miles, with an intermediate stop at Ipswich. The loads of the fastest trains were usually around 325 tons, but heavier loads were taken on some of the other services. I must confess, however, that excellent though their performance was, the 'Britannias' were not, in my experience, the most pleasurable locomotives on which to ride. Compared to the easy buoyant riding of Gresley and Stanier Pacifics they were very hard in their action. One was very conscious of riding on a piece of very massive ironmongery whereas the older Pacifics at their best 'rode like a dining car' as the saying went. The welcome the 'Britannias' had on the Great Eastern was probably not unconnected with the engines previously in use there. The 'Sandringham' class 3-cylinder 4-6-os at their best were very smooth and comfortable engines, but they could be wildly rough when the mileage had mounted up, while the Thompson 'B1s' were among the roughest and most uncomfortable engines on which I have ever had the misfortune to ride. I still have the notebook in which I apostrophised one of them—in East Anglia—as 'a vicious kicking little brute'!

Even so, the Great Eastern men were discerning enough when it came to other types. During the short period in 1951 when all their 'Britannias' were withdrawn, someone had the idea of putting a few of the grossly under-utilised Bulleid 'West Country' Pacifics to some fast revenue earning service. In tractive capacity they were not unlike the 'Britannias', but the Great Eastern men could make little of them. At the same time, when the 'Britannias' did return to their normal duties, in East Anglia and elsewhere, while the serious defect of wheels shifting on axles had been completely eradicated, the engines were still very prone to slipping, sometimes in the most unexpected and unaccountable circumstances. Slipping on starting from rest, or

47

when climbing a heavy gradient when adhesion is poor due to rain, or frost on the rails, was common enough with a great variety of locomotives, but when your 'steed' suddenly erupts, as it were, when running at 75 to 80mph on plain straight line, it is definitely not nice! The Bulleid Pacifics used to do it sometimes with the Continental boat trains down in the Weald of Kent, and it was there, of course, that the mishap with *William Shakespeare* occurred. But I had a most extraordinary experience riding up from Ipswich to Liverpool Street one afternoon on *Sir Christopher Wren*. It slipped first at full speed near Marks Tey, and thereafter it seemed the wheels could scarcely grip the rails at all, and at one stage slipping continued *after steam was shut off*. The engine was very carefully examined afterwards, but nothing untoward was found to account for this display of temperament.

In 1952 a further batch of twenty 'Britannias' was built at Crewe. Five of them, Nos 70025–9 were named after former Great Western 'Star' class 4-6-0s, and were allocated to Canton shed, Cardiff. Five went to the London Midland Region, and the remaining ten were divided between the Eastern and the London Midland. On the latter Region the new engines were put into links hitherto worked by Class '6' and '7' 4-6-0s, both on the ex-LNWR lines and on the Midland. Thus one found them working turn and turn about with 'Converted Scots' on the Irish Mails, and on the Euston–Manchester runs, and on certain Midland services from St Pancreas. From the data provided by a great number of logged runs there did not appear to be a great deal to choose between the '7P' 4-6-0s and the '7MT' Pacifics, though time was to show that the 'Britannias' were able to run considerably greater mileages between visits to shops for general repairs. Their repair cost per mile was also substantially less than that of the 'Converted Scots'.

It was another matter in South Wales. The five 'Britannias' named after 'Stars' took over the principal express workings from Canton shed from a very favoured and highly prized set of

'Castles' which generally had the reputation of being the best kept express engines on the Western Region. The local running superintendent saw to it that the new engines were treated with the utmost respect. There was to be no disdaining of them because they were not of Western design, and with this careful guidance they came to do steady and reliable work. But the schedules were not very demanding, such as 149 min non-stop for the 133·4 miles from Newport to Paddington. Much harder work, with similar loads, was needed on the Irish Mails between Crewe and Euston. Their propensity to slip was a handicap sometimes on the Western Region. One of them slipped itself to a stop in the Severn Tunnel, and had to be assisted out, and a similar misfortune befell another of them in Box Tunnel. Again, however, as in comparison with the 'Converted Royal Scots', their mileages between repairs, and their repair costs per mile came to show up to advantage against those of the 'Castles'.

Taken all round, while in these subtle, and more significant respects the 'Britannias' were proving better engines than the existing regional types, it cannot be said that in the mid-1950s they were making any definite impact upon either the Western or the London Midland motive power situation. So far as handling the traffic was concerned they showed no advantage over a 'Scot' or a 'Castle', and both these designs had the advantage of being more sure-footed in adverse rail conditions. On the Great Eastern line their triumph was absolute, not only in the absence of opposition of comparable power, but in their actual achievement, which was superb on every count. Their utilisation in East Anglia was a classic example of what could be done with the steam locomotive, when used in a specialised, carefully concentrated application. Where there were mixed links, or mixed studs at important sheds, individual likes and dislikes inevitably entered into it, and this was undoubtedly the case where 'Britannias' were working alongside 'Scots' and 'Castles'.

Of the smaller BR Pacifics of the '6MT', or 'Clan' class, it is difficult to write. To an outsider especially writing very much in retrospect, it is easy to question why this group of medium powered engines ever came to be built, and particularly with the 4-6-2 wheel arrangement. They were something completely outside the standard ranges postulated by the LMS and the LNER before nationalisation, and had a nominal tractive effort roughly equal to that of the LMS 'Jubilees' and 'Baby Scots' and of the Great Western 'Stars'. I have always understood that when the question of a class '6' mixed traffic engine was under discussion by the Railway Executive that consideration was given both to the 4-6-0 and the 4-6-2 wheel arrangement. The principal argument put forth in favour of the 4-6-2 was that the lower combustion rates resulting from the larger firegrate would result in economies large enough to offset the higher first cost of a Pacific over a 4-6-0. The performance of the 'West Country' Pacific of the Southern in the interchange trials of 1948 was freshly in mind, and although the proposed new standard Pacific was not quite in the same power class and had a poor overall efficiency the *impressement* it had caused was enough to top the scales. The projected '6MT' Pacific was originally intended for the Highland line, but in view of the known propensities of Pacifics in general to slipping, why—oh why?—did it have no more than 56¾ tons adhesion weight! The Jubilees had 60 tons.

The dice seemed to be loaded against the 'Clans' from the outset. It is perhaps just as well that they were not put on to the Highland line otherwise we might have had a northern counterpart to the humiliating situation that developed on the Somerset & Dorset line with the Bulleid 'West Country' Pacifics. Because of their unreliability from slipping on the banks, those potentially higher power locomotives were eventually subjected to the same load limits as the Stanier 'Black Fives' between Bath and Evercreech Junction. From my own experience between Carlisle and Glasgow on the former Caledonian route I very much doubt if the 'Clans' could have taken any greater loads than the 'Black Fives' over the heavy gradients between Perth and Inverness. In his book *British Railways Standard Steam Locomotives*, E. S. Cox naturally does his best to defend the reputation of the 'Clans', but when I rode with several of them on the footplate over that difficult route I found them deficient in the very feature that had dominated the decision to adopt the 4-6-2 wheel arrangement—in other words they were poor steamers. And a bad steaming engine was something that could not be tolerated in the 1950s.

Among the other standard engines, lower down the power range, the curiosity was the Class '4MT' 4-6-0. Why it was necessary to have a '4MT' 4-6-0 and a '4MT' 2-6-0 I do not know. The latter was an excellently hotted up development of the LMS '3000' class, unkindly nicknamed the 'Doodlebugs', from their ultra-modern and somewhat unprepossessing appearance. The BR standard '4MT' 2-6-0 was a smart little job that did much first class work. So indeed did the similarly powered 4-6-0, of which the first was built at Swindon; but I repeat, why was this latter engine necessary? I shall always remember an occasion at the Institution of Locomotive Engineers, in London, when a paper was read outlining the programme of standard locomotive construction. There was some rather plain speaking in the ensuing discussion and one young engineer, on the staff of British Railways, went so far as to suggest that the 'Clan' and the '4MT' 4-6-0 should be withdrawn, as unnecessary. It may be no more than a coincidence that not many months later he left British Railways and joined a firm in the supply trade; but with the benefit of hindsight one feels that he was right.

It was perhaps no more than natural that the '5MT' 4-6-0 made little individual impact. It was so obviously a close copy of the 'Black Five' albeit changed somewhat in outward appearance to have the distinctive family look of the standard engines; and its performance in service was similar in every way. In overall behaviour their performance in respect of repair costs per mile was closely similar, though those attached to the London Midland Region showed a rather greater mileage between general repairs than those of the Stanier engines. Whether one was comparing strictly like for like I do not know, for in 1957 the complete stud of Stanier 'Black Fives' on the LMR included many units that were then more than 20 years old. Like the Staniers the BR '5MTs' were very fast engines, and many instances were recorded with them of speeds between 85 and 90mph on the Glasgow–Aberdeen route.

Where the BR '5MT' 4-6-0s really did make an impact was on the Eastern Section of the Southern Region to which a number of them were allocated in replacement of 'King Arthur' class 4-6-0s that were being withdrawn. The Southern engine-men took to them at once, and got some great work out of them. The older engines being withdrawn were the Urie 'Arthurs', and it was a happy inspiration to perpetuate the names of those old favourites on Nos 73080–9 and 73110–19. The order of naming was not in the same sequence as that of the original ex-LSWR engines. At least one of the named BR Class '5MTs' No 73086 *The Green Knight* has achieved near-immortality in being acquired by David Shepherd, the great wildlife and railway artist, and is maintained in full working order on his own railway at Cranmore, Somerset. And referring to Cranmore brings me to what were the most outstanding of all the BR standard locomotives, the magnificent '9F' 2-10-0s. During their tragically short life these engines made more than an impact; they made a sensation. David Shepherd has one of them, 92203. It was not originally named, but at the time of its purchase the 'Britannia' No 70008 *Black Prince* was either on the point of withdrawal or actually retired, and Shepherd had the inspiration of naming his great engine *Black Prince*, as a fitting shed mate at Cranmore to *The Green Knight*. Of the '9Fs' in service there is much to write in a later chapter of this book.

FIRST STEPS IN TRANSITION

Above: The pioneer British diesel-electric main line locomotive, the ex-LMS No 10000, temporarily transferred to the Southern Region and working the down Bournemouth Belle near Winchfield. (*M. W. Earley*)

Below: The Metro-Vick gas turbine locomotive No 18100 on the Western Region Merchant Venturer passing Chippenham. (*K. H. Leech*)

MORE EX-LMS TYPES

Above: 'Converted Royal Scot' 4-6-0 No 46133 *The Green Howards* leaves
St Pancras with a Leeds express. (*British Railways*)
Below: Class '2' Ivatt 2-6-0 No 46471 on an Ulverston-Durham special
leaving Tebay. (*E. D. Bruton*)

5 Pressures for Modernisation

The British Railways standard locomotives took to the road for the first time at a very unpropitious moment in transport history. And the times did not get any better as they settled down to their allocated duties. Riddles' decision to concentrate on steam for the time being was anything but a popular one, even within British Railways. The enthusiasts were of course overjoyed, but they did not have the authority behind them, nor did their travelling contribute much to British Railways' funds. The public, starved of anything new by the years of wartime austerity, and cynical of the eventual results of railway nationalisation, regarded the perpetuation of steam as so much lack of vision, an inability to think beyond the precepts of George Stephenson. The popular press to whom 'knocking the railways' was an age-old sport, was generally hostile, and compared the patient, logical programme and sound economics of Riddles' policy to the tremendous enterprise of the American railways in sweeping steam away, almost overnight. Ours was timorous and reactionary.

A more serious cause of disquiet began to germinate in the many and varied firms of the railway manufacturing industry. I was in the thick of it myself, and heard it from many sides. Riddles' policy gave very little to British industry. All the new locomotives were to be built in railway shops. There was nothing violently new in this, but it was recalled that during the great 'scrap and build' programme of the LMS in the 1930s large batches of the new standard locomotives were built by contractors. It is true that immediately after the war, and for some years afterwards the great locomotive building firms were very busy with overseas orders. Railways in the Dominions were busy making up arrears of constructions that had been inevitable during the war. But the more farsighted managements, through the superb policy of after-sales' service pursued by British firms, and their invaluable contacts, realised that the whole trend everywhere was slowly but inexorably setting against steam—except in Great Britain. The situation was felt very keenly in the associated supply industries. While steam remained, and no more enterprising policies were being formulated than a restoration of the standards of pre-war years, there was little likelihood of more sophisticated modern equipment being needed; aware of what was happening elsewhere in the world there was a feeling that Great Britain was falling behind.

As in World War I the intense preoccupation of British industry with the needs of the armed forces, and the reduction of our export trade to a mere fraction of its pre-war volume had produced the acute risk that some vital markets might be lost for ever, and the risk was nowhere greater than with railway rolling stock. The enormous export trade that Great Britain once enjoyed in steam locomotives was built up on a two-fold reputation: first that the British home railways were the finest and incomparably the safest in the world, and second that the traditions of good design and excellent workmanship in the private building companies was an echo of the standards maintained and constantly expected on the home railways—and thus a guarantee of the best that could be purchased everywhere. In the years immediately following the end of World War II the reputation of the British locomotive manufacturing industry was secure enough where steam locomotives were concerned, but what of diesels? A home market in the new railway situation evolving out of nationalisation would have been an ideal sheet-anchor to a vigorous marketing drive for diesels abroad. In the last year before nationalisation, with the LMS ordering two large main line diesel-electric locomotives for trial against steam seemed a move in the right direction, but this move was halted by the motive power policy announced by the Railway Executive.

Developments in North America were certainly spectacular. The commercial introduction of the diesel-electric locomotive for main line service dates from 1936, but until the war years its headway, though considerable, was not very great in relation to the great assemblage of steam power on the railways of the USA. During the war, by Government decree, construction of new locomotives was confined to one manufacturer, General Motors, to avoid duplication of effort, but while this was justifiable as a wartime measure, it gave a tremendous fillip to GM production experience and capacity, and put the firm in a very strong position for post-war development. The American love of anything new favoured the prospects for a complete change in motive power policy, and the fact that diesel-electric locomotives then cost some $2\frac{1}{2}$ times that of a steam locomotive of the same nominal horsepower was rated of no consequence. Apart from direct purchase by some railway administrations finance was readily forthcoming to facilitate the introduction of diesels elsewhere on a lease-lend type of contract. Technically, nominal horsepower was not a fair basis on which to compare relative costs, because at low speeds, such as those at which mountain gradients were normally climbed—15 to 20mph—the drawbar pull of a diesel was roughly double that of a steam locomotive, of the same nominal horsepower. The drawbar pull did not become equal until the speed reached about 40mph. Above that the advantage moved slightly in favour of steam.

The upshot of all this was that construction of steam locomotives for the American railways ceased altogether in 1949, and the 'scrap and build' campaign worked up to its maximum intensity. In 1951, when the first British standard steam locomotives were taking the road there were still about 26,000 steam locomotives in revenue earning service in the USA, but the 15,000 diesel-electrics were by then handling considerably more than half the total traffic, in terms of ton miles, and the race was on to eliminate steam altogether. It was repeatedly being emphasised for the benefit of British readers that in cases of multiple-heading there was no need to have separate crews on each unit. A posse of four or five locomotives could be controlled by one crew. Furthermore, a diesel was always ready for duty. No preparation time was necessary, and as a consequence diesel units could be allocated to duties with a minimum of standby time between successive turns. By way of 'sales resistance' to the former contention it was pointed out that on a nationwide basis the amount of assistant engine mileage in Great Britain was really very small, and that the savings in crews possible by multiple operation, on hilly routes, would be minimal. Nevertheless the experience of the US railroads was quoted ad nauseam, and some of this propaganda began to impress the non-technical senior officers of the British Transport Commission.

British Railways were losing money—public money it was emphasised—and gradually the opinion began to harden that it was all the fault of steam. It was dirty, it was antiquated, and then came a new ploy—the sociologists began to exclaim that it was undignified for a man to have to shovel coal all day to earn his living. In many areas in Britain the railways had been slow in recovering from the effects of the war. In certain parts of the London commuter zones the local tank engines were in poor shape. Morale was low. Services had to be cancelled because of crew absentee-ism. 'It was all the fault of steam!' Then the news began to get round that Continental railways were rapidly modernising. While business interests 'plugged' the advance of the diesel in America, the first waves of British tourists to visit the Continent found smart new electric and diesel trains, and immediately there were adverse comparisons with conditions at home. The fact that the Southern Region was coping with the world's busiest suburban electrification, and had been for many years, was taken for granted, and the chronic overcrowding at peak hours was stoically accepted. But when the ever-venturesome O. V. S. Bulleid had the bright idea of double-deck coaches, the long suffering Southern season ticket holders were not amused; neither were the operating staff!

On certain routes regular travellers had seen non-steam forms of motive power come and go. On the Western Region there were the two experimental gas turbine locomotives, which un-tutored members of the general public were apt to regard as the shape of things to come, and a welcome move away from steam. One incident remains vividly in mind as showing the popular sentiments of the day. At that time I was a regular traveller, nearly every day on the 7.45 am express from Bristol to Padding-ton, between Bath and Chippenham. It was very much a prestige job for Old Oak shed, and always had an engine in first class condition. Until 1951 it was almost invariably a 'Castle', but then occasionally we got a 'Britannia'. Both the Brown Boveri, and the Metro-Vick gas turbine locomotives used to work this train, sometimes regularly for a while until their next breakdown. But the occasion that remains in my mind concerns a middle-aged commercial traveller with a rich Cockney accent who was a frequent passenger on the train from Bath to Paddington. Before the morning in question the Brown Boveri gas turbine had been on the job continuously for several days; but then as we waited on the platform in came the train hauled by a 'Britannia', and this character turned to his companion, saying: 'Struth, we've got the old 'ornby again'!

Although outwardly the policy of the Railway Executive might have appeared reactionary a great deal was going on beneath the surface. The British Transport Commission, and particularly its chairman, Lord Hurcomb, were far from convinced of the wisdom of the decision to retain steam. There was a strong feeling at Commission level that the mechanical and electrical engineers' department of the Executive was not taking full advantage of some 20 years study and experience of diesel traction, and of the visits that individual engineers from the British main line railways had paid to the United States. The Commission seemed to think that the engineers of the Railway Executive should know all the answers, whereas actual experience in running diesel units was confined to shunting engines on the LMS, and railcars with mechanical transmission on the Great Western. Experience with main line locomotives had only just begun. Lord Hurcomb had been very disappointed that a scheme of the former LNER to replace steam on the East Coast route with diesels had been abandoned after nationalisation, and in December 1948 at his request a committee on Types of Motive Power had been set up to report fully where the ultimate balance of advantage for British Railways would lie, as between steam, diesel, gas turbine, and electric traction. As usual with such committees their deliberations took a long time, and it was not until more than three years later that their report was presented. Mean while, of course, Riddles had gone ahead with his programme of steam locomotive standardisation.

The railway industry was aware of what was going on behind the scenes, and every possible pressure was brought to bear to try and secure a reversal of the initial decision of the Railway Executive to concentrate on steam; and there is no doubt that a good deal of backstage lobbying took place in the intervening years. How far these outside pressures influenced the nature of the Types of Motive Power Committee report it is not possible to say; but when it was completed it included three main recommendations:

1. Main line electrification from King's Cross to Grantham.
2. A large-scale trial of diesel traction on main line services elsewhere.
3. Replacement of steam on cross-country and branch lines by diesel railcars.

It was significant that no representative of the mechanical and electrical engineers' department of the Railway Executive was a member, and when the report was issued—for internal use only—the Railway Executive rejected the second proposal, and while agreeing with the principle of main line electrification, did not think that King's Cross–Grantham was suitable for its first application.

The circulation of this report, and the generally adverse reception it received at the hands of the Railway Executive caused a distinct cleavage in the higher circles of the nationalised transport administration. While it would not be entirely true to say that the Types of Motive Power Committee had been swayed to some extent by the experience of its chairman some years earlier on a fact-finding mission to the USA studying diesel traction, the non-technical members of the committee, not concerned with the practical problems of getting diesel traction launched, were inclined to think that all American geese were swans. On the other hand Riddles, with the solid experience of the first two main line diesel-electric locomotives of the LMS at his fingertips, was able to explain that they were costing more to operate as single units in high-mileage rosters than the 'Duchess' class Pacifics. These original LMS diesels were of 1600 horsepower, and on the heaviest duties which a Pacific could handle without assistance, both diesels were needed coupled in multiple. In the conditions of financial stringency that then prevailed was there any point in spending some £7 million on a hundred diesel-electric locomotives of 2000 horsepower?

It was unfortunate that at this very time the mechanical troubles with the 'Britannia' class locomotives should have occurred, though in certain quarters they did no more than add a little to the general stigma attached to steam, rather than blacklist the new range of standard locomotives. Nevertheless, while the unprofitable game of 'pull devil pull baker' was being played within the precincts of 222 Marylebone Road, the staging of the Festival of Britain and the introduction of a new series of named express passenger trains acted as a tonic to many of the rank and file of the railway service, and a focus point of interest for the travelling public. Some such tonic was needed, in all conscience! I have referred more than once already in this book to the deterioration in morale following nationalisation. I may mention a single incident from the Western Region and what the introduction of a Festival train did for it. In the summer of 1949 engine No 7019 *Fowey Castle*, new out of Swindon, was allocated to Bristol, Bath Road shed. She was clearly a good strong engine, but as the months went by she got filthier and filthier, looking as if she had never seen a cleaner's rag from the day she was outshopped from Swindon. When I had an engine pass to ride the Wolverhampton-Penzance express, particularly to observe the working of the three-row superheater 'Castles', Stafford Road shed did not have one available, and they borrowed 7019 from Bristol. It would have been difficult to find a patch of green anywhere on her. She was just coated with grime.

The duty was then double-manned, with an Exeter crew relieving the Stafford Road men at Bristol, and on both stages of the run she responded well and gave an excellent performance. But what an old crab she looked! Then in 1951 The Merchant Venturer was introduced. It was of course no more than the time-honoured 11.15am from Paddington to Bath, Bristol and Weston-super-Mare, and the return working of the same rake of coaches at 5.25pm from Bristol. The down train was sometimes worked by an Old Oak 'Britannia', though usually by a 'Castle', but the return was a regular Bristol 'mileage link' job, returning from Paddington on the West of England Postal. Until the naming of the up train the turn was worked variously by 'Castles', 'Counties', and sometimes even by 'Stars'. When the 5.25pm up from Bristol became The Merchant Venturer all the traditional Great Western pride in the job returned, and 7019 of all engines was taken, cleaned, polished and burnished till she would have been fit for the Royal Train! She worked The Merchant Venturer for some time during the summer of 1951.

Except on the Great Eastern Line the Festival named trains were worked by regional classes of locomotive, and it was only on special occasions that a Standard would be allocated. This took place when there was a press visit to Rugby locomotive testing station, and the guests were taken down from Euston in a special train, including the Horwich dynamometer car, and hauled by a new 'Britannia' No 70009 *Alfred the Great*. I was one of those privileged to go, and at Rugby we saw another of the 'Britannias', No 70005, going hard on the stationary plant. During the day, in talks with Riddles, and his two principal lieutenants R. C. Bond, and E. S. Cox, I learned something of the programme that was being launched for the systematic testing, not only of the new engines but of many others. It was clear then that the policy of the Railway Executive envisaged the continued use of steam for some time to come. No hint came that day of the shadows that were beginning to close in upon the long and honourable saga of British steam.

6 The Standards versus the Regionals

Taking my cue from that interesting day at Rugby I am leaving all the undercurrents on one side for at least one chapter, and concentrating on the absorbing and often stimulating events of the years 1952–4. This was the time when British railways really began to fight back to something like their old standards of locomotive performance, though for the men at the top it was a time of anxiety and frustration, following a change of Government, and the threat of major organisational changes—unfortunately the first of many! In the regions, however, with the first impacts of nationalisation duly weathered, something of the old railway spirit revived, together with a resurgence of regional loyalties. Intense interest was created by the establishment of truly scientific methods of engine testing, which the Railway Executive based on the practice that had been evolved over many years by the Great Western Railway. This was not to the liking of certain highly placed engineers whose earlier work was on the LMS, but the Railway Executive had come to appreciate the greater practical value of testing locomotives at constant rates of steam production rather than at constant speed.

With S. O. Ell in charge of locomotive testing at Swindon, and having himself virtually perfected the system of constant steam rate working postulated first by C. E. Roberts, and developed by W. J. Dymond, the Western Region of the 1950s came once more into the very heart of British locomotive development, and all lovers of the old Great Western Railway who were privileged to ride in the dynamometer car were pleased to see the portrait of G. J. Churchward on one of its walls. In another respect than that of old traditions and memories, Sam Ell and his team at Swindon had an advantage over their counterparts in the new stationary plant at Rugby. They had the ex-GWR dynamometer car and the same team that tested locomotives on the stationary plant went out to do the corroborative work on the line. D. R. Carling and his staff at Rugby, working under the direct authority of the Railway Executive had no corresponding facilities. The corroborating road tests were carried out by the testing staff of the London Midland Region, based at Derby, and at first using the Horwich dynamometer car. The road trials took place mostly between Skipton and Carlisle.

To the delight of all serious students of locomotive design and its associated performance, the Railway Executive decided to make the results of these trials public, in a series of splendidly produced and fully authoritative bulletins. As they came out, one by one, something of the controversies of the 1948 interchange trials were revived, as a result of closely controlled, highly disciplined testing, instead of the 'hit or miss' methods of 1948 when personalities, local railway politics and goodness knows what else intruded to help obscure the true issues. It is perhaps significant of the needs of the day that most of the engines tested on one or other of the stationary plants were of the mixed traffic types. Perhaps the most interesting of all, in view of the related situation in 1948, were those of the Class '5' 4-6-0s: 'Hall'; 'B1', and a new BR '5'. The first of these was tested at Swindon; the other two, after stationary tests at Rugby did their running trials over the Settle and Carlisle line. I am afraid however that the following figures extracted very carefully from the voluminous published reports, will not please Great Western enthusiasts!

STEAM RATE 20,000LB PER HOUR

Engine class	Hall	B1	5MT
Coal, lb per hour	3020	2750	2840
Drawbar horsepower at			
30mph	1070	1100	1130
40mph	1030	1150	1130
50mph	1000	1150	1110
60mph	890	1100	1070
70mph	680	1000	1000
Coal per dbhp hour at			
40mph	2·92	2·4	2·5

STEAM RATE 15,000LB PER HOUR

	Hall	B1	5MT
Coal lb per hour	1860	1800	1920
Drawbar horsepower at			
30mph	720	800	830
40mph	710	800	810
50mph	650	775	760
60mph	520	720	700
70mph	350	620	605
Coal per dbhp hour at			
40mph	2·65	2·35	2·6

All three locomotives were being fired on Blidworth coal, a second grade fuel considered as a good yardstick for measuring the performance of mixed traffic engines. At the high steam rate of 20,000lb/hr roughly the maximum for all three classes of locomotive, the 'Hall' was the least economical, while the power output fell off very rapidly above 50mph. Up to that speed there was not a great deal of difference, with the 'Hall' a little behind the other two, but whereas the BR standard '5MT' fell only from 1110 at 50mph to 1000 at 70mph, the 'Hall' fell from 1000 to 680. The fall was even more pronounced at the lower steam rate of 15,000lb/hr, to an output of no more than 350 at the drawbar at 70mph. The engine in question was one of the

Hawksworth variety, with the rather higher degree of superheat. Although no comment on this was made in the bulletin, it could have been due to the valve setting characteristics of the Stephenson link motion.

The really striking point about this comparison is the remarkably fine showing made by the ex-LNER 'B1' returning not only the lowest basic coal consumption, but in conjunction with very fine power outputs. This aptly corroborated the fine work done by engines of this class in the interchange trials of 1948, particularly between Bristol and Plymouth, though there were other factors that weighed against the special features of the 'B1' being incorporated in the standard range of BR locomotives. The boiler was that of the Gresley 'Sandringham' class. It was considerably cheaper in first cost than the sophisticated Stanier design on the ex-LMS 'Black Five', but heavier in maintenance charges. Furthermore, the chassis design, bearing construction, and arrangements for balancing led to rapid deterioration, and a very rough engine. The thermodynamic performance, as exemplified by the foregoing test results was nevertheless very fine indeed.

A very important part of the work on both stationary testing plants was to lay bare and try to eradicate unsatisfactory features of design and performance, and a notable instance of this concerned the celebrated 'V2' 2-6-2 of the former LNER. In the drive to minimise attention needed to locomotives when on shed the LMS in the last years before nationalisation had introduced deflector plates, and screens in the smokeboxes of certain modern classes to produce a self-cleaning effect. These proved satisfactory though their interposition had the side effect of impairing the draught action, and reducing the steaming capacity. Slight alterations to the blastpipe dimensions and positioning generally put such matters to rights, though the effect of the self-cleaning plates proved more hindering when they were applied to other locomotive classes. The 'V2' was one of these, and an engine was sent to Swindon for examination. Sam Ell and his men had become specialists in draughting, and they introduced revised proportions, both of the blastpipe and the shape of the chimney—internally of course. The result was that the modified engine steamed as freely with the self-cleaning plates in, as the original design had done without them.

Meanwhile, there had been a general switch round of chief mechanical engineers, following the retirement of Bulleid, Hawksworth, Ivatt, and Peppercorn. After some intermediate appointments, Riddles had made the following moves:

Region	Mechanical and Electrical engineer	Former railway
Eastern	} K. J. Cook	GWR
North Eastern		
London Midland	J. F. Harrison	LNER
Scottish	M. S. Hatchell	Southern
Southern	S. B. Warder	—
Western	R. A. Smeddle	LNER

The influence of the former LMS remained strong at headquarters, but the new appointments in the E&NE and Western Regions had some interesting sequels.

Bulleid's retirement had undoubtedly left the Railway Executive with its biggest headaches, so far as existing motive power was concerned. The air-smoothed Pacifics of both 'Merchant Navy' and 'West Country' classes were capable of tremendous outputs of power, when their machinery was well tuned up; but even at the best of times they were addicted, perhaps more than any other British Pacifics to fits of uncontrolled slipping, for which leakage from the oil bath in which their special chain-driven valve gear was encased was partly responsible. But there were so many features of the design that were troublesome in themselves and which cut diametrically across the standards that had been found satisfactory and necessary elsewhere, that some investigations and possible rebuilding had to be considered. Full dress trials on the stationary testing plant at Rugby, and on the Settle & Carlisle line had given some results that were certainly odd, in respect of behaviour of the valve gear, and the slipping at times was severe enough to bend side rods. There was even talk of scrapping the lot, at one time. I need not dwell upon the unfortunate episode of the 'Leader' class engines, Bulleid's extraordinary adventure into the unorthodox, which ended in November 1949, with orders from the Railway Executive to stop all work on the project.

Bulleid had been personal assistant to Sir Nigel Gresley during the exciting, colourful, and highly spectacular development of high speed trains on the LNER during the 1930s, and he was as much aware as any man living of the difficulties experienced with the conjugated valve gear used on the inside cylinder of all Gresley's three-cylinder designs. The trouble was slop in the pin joints forming the linkage from the outside to the inside valve spindles, which became progressively worse as mileage increased, and wear developed. Although a linkage including a number of pin joints was inherently subject to this trouble, it was made worse by the manufacturing facilities available at Doncaster. During the slump years of the 1930s no funds were available for modernisation of the plant, and locomotives were built with clearances in the bearing appropriate to the degree of accuracy with which the frames could be set up. After his translation from Swindon to the Eastern and North Eastern Regions, K. J. Cook installed the system of optical lining up of frames and cylinder centre lines that had enabled such precision to be built into Great Western Locomotives. This was applied to the various three-cylinder classes, and enabled the running gear to be assembled with much tighter clearances in the bearings. The characteristic Gresley ring disappeared, and the 'A3' and 'A4' Pacifics in particular were able to do a great deal of very fine work in the last ten years of their lives, quite up to pre-war standard, and without the anxiety of overheated middle big-ends. These latter were changed to the modified de Glehn

69

type, as used in the inside big-ends of Great Western locomotives, and those of the LMS that were of Stanier design.

The question of adhesion, and liability of Pacifics to slip when rail conditions were unfavourable, had come very much to the fore when the trouble of wheels shifting on axles occurred with the 'Britannias'. At the time the latter engines were being designed a heavy freight equivalent was in prospect, of the 2-8-2 type. This was an echo of Gresley who built two engines of the latter type, with boiler and many parts standard with his first Pacifics. The Gresley 'P1' engines, however, were fitted with boosters on the trailing truck, and were intended only for the heavy coal traffic between Peterborough and Ferme Park, Harringay. In considering a 2-8-2 the engineers of the Railway Executive had in mind the gradual elimination of unbraked freight trains, and the need to provide for fast fully-fitted trains that could give a closely timed overnight service between major centres of industry. On the former LNER the 'V2' had been introduced with that in view. On the other hand during his distinguished service with the War Department in 1940-4 Riddles had designed and operated the very successful 2-10-0, and some exploratory drawing office work showed that a wide firebox could be accommodated above 5ft diameter coupled wheels, so the BR standard heavy freight locomotive became a 2-10-0—the remarkable '9F', or 92000 class.

The first thirty of these engines were built at Crewe in 1953, of which 18 were allocated to the Western, 5 to the Eastern, and the remainder to the London Midland Region. On their introduction a change was made in the practice adopted with the 'Britannias', all of which, whatever their allocation, were maintained by the LM Region, at Crewe. From the outset the '9Fs' were maintained by the region to which they were allocated. With the introduction of the '9Fs' there began one of the most extraordinary histories in the entire records of the steam locomotive. After the announcement of the great Modernisation Plan in 1955, including the complete elimination of steam as soon as

SOUTHERN PACIFICS

Above: One of the 'West Country' class, Pacifics No 34106 *Lydford*, in original condition, on the Plymouth-Brighton express leaving Seaton Junction in September 1959. (*Derek Cross*)

Below: Rebuilt 'Merchant Navy' No 35028 *Clan Line* on the down Atlantic Coast Express about to cross from the Bournemouth to Exeter routes at Worting Junction in March 1960. This engine has since been preserved. (*Derek Cross*)

WESTERN REGION HISTORY

Above: One of the first 'Britannias' attached to Old Oak shed, No 70018 *Flying Dutchman* at Bristol after working the pre-accelerated Bristolian, face to face with 4-6-0 No 7029 *Clun Castle*. (*K. H. Leech*)

Below; Clun Castle as rebuilt with double chimney and in private ownership, passing Penrith on an LCGB special to Carlisle on 14 October 1967. (*Derek Cross*)

practicable, the total of new locomotives built continued much the same until the end of 1957. The totals for 1955/6/7 were 156, 129, and 141 respectively and of those totals '9F' 2-10-0s accounted for 38, 45 and 56 respectively. By that time the total for the whole class had risen to 171—all so far built at Crewe. After 1957 however as was logically to be expected in view of the Modernisation Plan and the impending deliveries of the first new diesels the construction of steam locomotives ceased—except for the '9Fs'. Crewe finished its existing orders bringing the total up to 178, and then construction was switched to Swindon. The actual building programme, which actually fell somewhat behind schedule ultimately, was 25 for the Eastern Region in 1956, and 48 for the Western. Of the latter 18 were booked for 1957 and 30 for 1958. Ten years later the whole stud had been withdrawn.

Such were the plain statistics of the story. In comment however one could use the Churchillian idiom and say that never in the whole history of the steam locomotive had such an outstanding design been put to so little use. One could have understood it if construction had ceased with that of the other standard designs at the end of 1957; but with the diesel revolution gaining momentum with every week that passed, Swindon works was busy turning out '9Fs' during 1958 at an average of more than one per week. Another 15 were completed in 1959 and the last 3 in 1960. One could well ask—why? In the very week that I was writing this chapter a great friend, who previously had shown no particular interest in locomotives took his grandson to Cranmore, and managed to spend a short time on the footplate of No 92203. He certainly came back appreciating a little of why the steam locomotive has always enthralled me; but more than anything else he was almost dumbfounded by the date of construction of the engine—'Nineteen fifty-nine, but that's only yesterday!' When one recalls the longevity of other famous British locomotives, Gresley Pacifics, 'King Arthurs', 'Castles', 'Kings', Midland compounds all topping the 30-year mark an enquiring stranger might well ask what was the matter with the

'9Fs' that they were withdrawn so soon. To reply that they were one of the finest steam locomotive designs of all time would seem to be plain daft; but so they were.

In this chapter may I just extol their merits, leaving the reasons for their early demise until later. There is no doubt that some members of the design staff of the Railway Executive would much have preferred a 2-8-2 on which they could have put the 'Britannia' boiler, and in the test bulletin relating to the '9F' there are some rather apologetic remarks about the steam production being as good as could be expected with so shallow a grate. But fired with Blidworth coal the '9F' was steamed up to a maximum of 30,000lb of steam per hour, against 31,410 for the 'Britannia', so that there was not a great deal in it. The test results showed that a '9F' steamed to its maximum could haul a 1000-ton train of loaded 16-ton mineral wagons at 52mph on level track, or at 35mph up a gradient of 1-in-200. What was not expected was the astonishing versatility of class, and the speed attained in passenger service. At least two fully authenticated records are available of '9F' engines attaining maximum speeds of 90mph—*ninety*, with ten coupled wheels of only 5ft 0in diameter!

Almost at the end of the steam era a few were used most successfully on the heavily graded Somerset & Dorset line, eliminating once and for all the need for double-heading on gradients of 1in50, even when the loads were as much as 450 tons. One imagines how well they would have done on the Highland main line, where the standard motive power from 1935 to the very end of steam was the Class '5'—first the Stanier 'Black Five', and then the BR '5MT' to help out when necessary in the last years. In cases of heavy loading these engines were used in pairs. A single '9F' could have managed any of the duties so worked. They ran steadily and comfortably up to 60mph in their ordinary work. I have not seen any footplate reports of what they were like at higher speeds, and their use on *express* passenger trains was officially frowned upon. It would have been no use asking for a footplate pass to ride one of them on The Red Dragon from Cardiff to Paddington, or still less on The Flying Scotsman from Grantham to King's Cross. It was on the latter train that an experienced recorder logged a run little different from normal running, including a maximum of 90mph at Essendine. It was not until they reached King's Cross and he walked to the front end that he discovered that it was not a Gresley Pacific but a '9F' that had taken over haulage of the train at Grantham!

7 1954—Year of Destiny

While many influences were at work to try and bring about a complete change in the motive power set-up on British Railways, the Executive, on the advice of Riddles, was still basing its policy on the continuation of steam for some time to come. The Regions were anxious to restore at least some of their best trains to pre-war standards of speed, which the upsurge of pride and national sentiment aroused by the coronation year of Her Majesty Queen Elizabeth II, had in part stimulated. And so, once again, attention became directed towards express passenger locomotives, which until the year 1953 had been largely outside the line of development fostered by Railway Executive headquarters. It is true that much attention had been given to the 'Merchant Navy' class, as referred to in the preceding chapter; but that was out of sheer necessity, rather than with any prospect of substantial acceleration of service in view. On the other hand the rejuvenation of the Gresley Pacifics helped towards the acceleration of the London–Edinburgh non-stops. It was essential to use the Gresley engines on these lengthy runs because of their lower coal consumption than the post-war Peppercorn type.

When the Western Region management called for acceleration first of the Bristolian and then a year later of the Cornish Riviera Express, Ell and his staff, under the enthusiastic direction of R. A. Smeddle, applied their increasingly wide experience of draughting problems to the 'King' class. Those famous engines, by then more than 25 years old, had been designed for an era long since past, when the Great Western Railway could be closely selective in the grades of coal it purchased for the crack main line duties. The problem in 1953 was to enable those engines to produce pre-war standards of performance on post-war fuel. This meant alteration to the draughting, and in so doing discarding certain cherished features of Swindon loco-motive practice, notably the jumper ring on the blastpipe. It was argued that a slight increase in the basic coal consump-tion was a small price to pay for reliability in steaming in the varying conditions of fuel supply in the 1950s. Ell took engine No 6001 *King Edward VII*, and by some very simple and cheaply made alterations to the blastpipe, and to the internal shape and proportions of the chimney, secured a remarkable increase in the maximum steaming capacity of the boiler, boost-ing it to a little over 30,000lb/hr—equal to the much larger boilers and fireboxes of the BR standard 'Britannias' and '9Fs'.

While the immediate object of this modification was to enable the Bristolian express to be restored to its pre-war timing of 1¾ hours non-stop between Paddington and Temple Meads a series of corroborative tests on the road at such speeds would have been difficult to fit into the ordinary traffic programme, and instead, in the path usually allocated to dynamometer car test runs between Reading and Stoke Gifford yard, adjacent to the site of the present Bristol Parkway station, the loads hauled by the locomotive were successively stepped up until it reached twenty-five main line corridor coaches. This was just about double the weight of an ordinary passenger train, and scaled a little short of 800 tons behind the tender. This was worked from Reading to Stoke Gifford and back at normal express train speeds of that period, making runs over the 74 miles between Scours Lane Junction, passed very slowly, and Stoke Gifford, of 80 minutes westbound, and 77 minutes coming up. On the slightly falling gradients between Swindon and Didcot on the eastbound this huge train was worked up to a steady speed of 70–71mph. It was indeed a magnificent performance which I was privileged to observe at first hand from the dynamometer car. The Bristolian was successfully accelerated to its old 1¾-hour run in 1954, and the Cornish Riviera Express to a 4-hour timing from Paddington to Plymouth a year later.

The 'Duchess' class Pacifics of the former LMS earned distinction in being among the very few British express locomotives that needed no modifications to fit them for the difficult working conditions of the 1950s. It is true that those that were originally streamlined had this questionable adornment removed, and smoke deflecting plates added, but no alteration was needed to their draughting, or details of their running gear or frames. In 1955 one of them was lent to the Western Region for trial running on the Cornish Riviera Express. It was worked by Western Region men and did very well, though within the maximum requirements of that service, no better, no more economically than a 'King' having the Ell modifications to its draughting. Up to a steam rate of around 30,000lb/hr the coal consumptions were practically identical, though in the following year when engine No 46225 *Duchess of Gloucester* was put through a complete series of trials on the stationary plant at Rugby, and afterwards on the line between Skipton and Carlisle, some remarkable feats of steam production and power output were achieved, albeit involving the employment of two firemen.

Although the steaming of both the 'King' and 'Duchess' boilers was so similar, when it came to converting this into power at the drawbar the advantage lay very much with the LMS engine. The 'King' showed a falling off in drawbar horsepower at the higher speeds that was noticed in the previous chapter in the comparison between the various mixed traffic 4-6-0s. The accompanying table shows a comparison between the 'King' and the 'Duchess', at a steam rate of 30,000lb/hr. On both engines this would have required a firing rate of 4000lb of coal per hour, and needing two firemen. The maximum accepted rate for a single fireman to sustain continuously was 3000lb per hour, though of course on most express runs the demand would fluctuate considerably, topping the 4000 mark for short periods and often falling to 2000lb per hour, or less. It was this adverse

OUTPUT AT 30,000LB OF STEAM PER HOUR

4000lb of coal per hour

Speed	Drawbar horsepower	
mph	King	Duchess
30	1640	1735
50	1540	1765
70	1190	1570

comparison that led R. A. Smeddle to obtain authority, for more extensive modernisation work on the 'Kings', following the competitive runs on the Cornish Riviera Express in 1955.

At the time when preparations were being made to ring out the death-knell of steam, it was remarkable that such striking evidence of its virility was being shown on so many of the major routes of Great Britain. On the London Midland Region no adjustments were needed to the draughting of the 'Duchess' 4-6-2s, or of the 'Princess Royals' for that matter, for them to take up the strenuous accelerated schedules of the Royal and Midday Scots, between Euston and Crewe, or of the 'Mersey-side Express' and the 'Red Rose'. The timing of no more than 80 minutes start-to-stop for the 82·6 miles from Euston to Rugby might have been regarded as something of a counsel of perfection with such loads as those two famous Anglo-Scottish expresses were carrying in 1954–5, but engines and crews took it in their stride. I still remember with a thrill the experience of riding *Duchess of Atholl*, at 67mph sustained up the 1in335 gradient past Harrow and Hatch End with a 510-ton train behind us, and of *City of Leeds*, of the same class sustaining

77mph on the level north of Blisworth with the same train on another occasion. In the years from 1954 onwards the ex-LMS Pacifics were doing some of the finest work of their whole existence.

And what of the Gresley 'A4s'? In 1953, in honour of Coronation Year, the summer London–Edinburgh non-stop had been renamed The Elizabethan, and given a timing of 405 minutes for the 392¾ miles between King's Cross and Waverley in each direction. In the summer of 1954 another 15 minutes were cut from the schedule, thus demanding an average speed of a little over 60mph. In pre-war years the streamlined Coronation of 1937 took the level six hours, but with a maximum load of 325 tons, and including two brief stops. The Elizabethan carried a load of 425 tons, with the added requirement of making the journey non-stop. Naturally the engines allocated to this duty were carefully selected units, but even with this qualification the performance was superb. The crews, from Haymarket and King's Cross sheds in partnership, made it a point of honour to run to time even if the journeys were beset by unforeseen or incidental delays en route. A journey I had on the southbound train soon after its introduction, in 1954, was typical rather than exceptional.

The engine was *Golden Fleece*, one of the two named specially for working the West Riding Limited steamliner in 1937, and the Scottish driver ran the train with precision, handing over to his King's Cross colleague who had travelled in the train thus far, and gained the footplate through the corridor tender, near Alne, just thirteen seconds inside schedule time, 193·3 miles from Edinburgh in 190 minutes 47 seconds. There were three slowings for permanent way work to come, in addition to one that had already been experienced and its effects recovered, and in anticipation the London driver got a little time in hand. I was privileged to spend some time on the footplate, and it all seemed so easy: the coal reasonably good; the boiler steaming freely, and the machinery of the engine singing along with the

ACTIVITIES AT SWINDON

Above: 'Warship' class diesel-hydraulic locomotive under construction beside 'Castles' under repair. (*British Railways*)

Below: The unique BR Class '8' 4-6-2 No 71000 *Duke of Gloucester* at speed on the stationary test plant. (*British Railways*)

SMALLER BR STANDARD TYPES

Above: BR Class '5' 4-6-0 No 73002, on an up Midland line express near
Elstree on 15 March 1952. (*E. D. Bruton*)
Below: A '3MT' standard 2-6-0 No 77015 on a Lanark-Muirkirk train
passes Glenbuck loch in March 1961. (*Derek Cross*)

Above: An early 'Britannia' working: engine No 70014 *Iron Duke* heads an up Bournemouth express near Winchfield. (*M. W. Earley*)
Below: BR Class '5' No 73031 temporarily fitted with the Westinghouse brake for freight train trials, heads a St Pancras-Nottingham express climbing Sharnbrook bank. (*Ian S. Pearsall*)

THE DIESEL INFILTRATION

Above: A Southern Region Margate-Charing Cross express (via Dover) climbs Hildenborough bank behind a Type 3 locomotive of D6500 class.
(*British Railways*)

Below: The up Mayflower, Western Region, in Sonning Cutting, hauled by North British Loco Co diesel-hydraulic locomotive No D602 in July 1959.
(*M. W. Earley*)

quiet elegance of a sewing machine. Down the famous descent from Stoke tunnel towards Peterborough where so many famous speed exploits have taken place, the engine was allowed to make her own pace, and swept easily up to a maximum of 96mph. To cut a long and exhilarating story short we reached King's Cross five minutes early, with an actual time from Edinburgh of 385 minutes, and a net time, allowing for the various checks, of no more than 369 minutes—21 minutes inside schedule and a net average speed of 64mph.

In 1952 there had occurred the terrible double collision at Harrow, the worst ever on English metals, one result of which was that the almost new Pacific engine No 46202 *Princess Anne* was damaged beyond repair. Instead of providing a straight replacement, Riddles obtained authority to build in its place a prototype Class '8' British standard express passenger Pacific, which eventually materialised as No 71000 *Duke of Gloucester*. As this engine was from the outset conceived as a one-off job, a pilot project to be run, tested, and analysed against the time when hopefully more Class '8' express passenger engines would be needed, the design was prepared to incorporate the maximum of parts that would be common to the BR standard range, and would involve the minimum of new tooling and patterns. Because the new engine was required to have a nominal tractive effort comparable with existing Class '8's the cylinder capacity was more than could be provided by the standard arrangement on the 'Britannias', though, in adopting three cylinders, special provision was taken against the possibility of trouble with the inside big-end. This was made of especially massive construction.

The decision to use Caprotti valves was a surprise to me personally, because although on theoretical grounds poppet valves gave a better steam distribution than piston valves, and yielded a very free-running engine, all British experience until the introduction of the Standards seem to have shown that the poppet valve engines, while giving a superlative performance when new, were subject to deterioration much more rapidly, with consequent increase in coal consumption. On the LNER, Gresley's first 'P2' *Cock o' the North* was hailed as one of the world's wonders, but very soon, in day-to-day working over the Edinburgh–Aberdeen route, it fell behind the splendid daily work of the rival engine with piston valves, *Earl Marischal*, and Gresley himself converted *Cock o' the North* to piston valves. Earlier, on the LMS, of the twenty ex-LNWR 'Claughtons' rebuilt with larger boilers, those having Caprotti valve gear were generally inferior in tractive power to the piston valve engines. It was significant that only the latter were allocated to the Preston–Carlisle route where hard work on the banks was necessary.

The same story was repeated, in my experience in a much more pronounced form, with the batch of ex-LMS 'Black Five' 4-6-0s fitted with Caprotti valve gear, and introduced in 1948. These engines were very fast, but terribly slow in accelerating, and weak on the banks. I shall never forget a footplate run I made from Leeds to Carlisle on one of them, in good weather, with an excellent crew, and a free steaming engine; yet when it came to climbing the 'Long Drag' from Settle Junction up to Blea Moor, I honestly think that with the 300-ton train we had, a Midland Class '2' superheated 4-4-0 could have done as well. I have before me a record of No 432 of this latter type sustaining 32mph up the final 1-in-100 to Ribblehead, with a load of 205 tons, yet the Caprotti '5', with full boiler pressure, and a full glass of water fell to 23mph with 300 tons. The respective drawbar horsepowers were 620 from the '5' and 650 from the Midland Class '2'. The Caprotti '5s' had a good record so far as repair costs were concerned but as tractive units they seemed singularly lacking in guts. In 1954, when the Institution of Locomotive Engineers visited Crewe Works the BR Class '8' engine No 71000 was on display, and I remember J. F. Harrison drawing me to one side and saying with all loyalty to his old railway and saying of 71000: 'I think Sir Nigel Gresley would approve.' I wondered; but the shortcomings of that prototype engine did not at the outset centre upon the valve gear—rather the reverse.

The engine was sent to Swindon in 1955 for trials on the stationary plant, and on the road, and like the majority of poppet valve locomotives when new, it returned a magnificent cylinder performance. I had the privilege of seeing it on the plant, and of riding in the dynamometer car behind it. Ell and his men had never recorded figures anything like it. It was however the boiler that provided the big surprise, of the opposite kind. The engine had the 'Britannia' boiler, but with a larger firebox giving a grate area of 48·6sq ft, against 42sq ft on the Class '7', and a twin orifice blastpipe and double chimney. All the ingredients of a mighty steam raiser were there; but fire as they might, Swindon could not obtain more than 30,000lb of steam per hour out of that boiler with Blidworth coal, and then at a very heavy coal consumption. I remember the first time I went to Swindon to see the engine in action, and how Ell remarked: 'She's a coal scoffer!' The basic proportions all seemed favourable enough, and it probably needed no more than some modifications to the draughting to put matters right. Ell sought authority to investigate, but it was not granted, why I have not been able to find out. Maybe in the year 1955 it was not thought worth while spending time on research into steam locomotive performance, when the decree had gone forth in the Modernisation Plan that steam must be phased out as quickly as possible. So No 71000 was returned to Crewe as built, and took her place in the Pacific link at the North Shed there. The workings of that link took its engines to Euston, Glasgow and Perth in which No 71000 was expected to take turns.

The result was much as could have been foreseen. The hard riding characteristic of BR Pacifics did not endear the engine to the footplate crews, who were used to the smooth and buoyant action of the 'Duchesses', while even at relative low power output the coal consumption was comparatively high, and the firing more arduous in any case. Engine No 71000 was certainly up against formidable competitors in this respect, because the 'Duchesses' were the easiest of all British Pacifics to fire. The coal had only to be eased in through the door, and the action of the engine spread it beautifully over that large grate, even into the back corners. It was not surprising therefore that No 71000 was not favoured for the long double-home turns worked from Crewe North, particularly on a job like the Inverness sleeper, with its heavy summer loads to be worked non-stop from Crewe to Motherwell over Shap and Beattock, and continuing thence to Perth. By my observations the engine worked mostly between Crewe and Euston and Crewe and Carlisle.

It was sad that the very last express passenger locomotive built for service in Great Britain should have proved something of an enigma. In writing of the British Railways standard steam locomotives E. S. Cox confesses that they never knew what was really the trouble with it, though from the treatment given to certain other tiresome classes, and the response obtained one could make a pretty fair guess what was wrong. Whether if this weakness had been pinpointed and rectified, the engine would have proved a 'world-beater', as Cox suggests, we shall never know. From the experience elsewhere with poppet valve locomotives—not forgetting those of Chapelon—I would be inclined to doubt it. But that any development work on the engine was dropped was unhappily typical of the situation in 1955. In closing the story of steam development, one leaves the enthusiast to decide, according to his particular fancies and his parameters for assessment, as to which were the greatest of all British express passenger locomotives—the 'Duchesses', the 'A4s', the 'Kings' or the 'Merchant Navies'. As things were in 1955 it was certainly not No 71000.

8 Modernisation—The End of Steam foreshadowed

When the Modernisation Plan of the British Transport Commission was announced in January 1955 one of its most important aspects may be quoted, thus: 'The progressive replacement of steam locomotives by electric and diesel traction, with all that is involved in new facilities and equipment at the main Works, new motive power and rolling stock maintenance depots and massive programmes of staff training.' Note the highly significant words 'progressive replacement'. This suggested an orderly and carefully considered plan, having regard to the programmes of steam locomotive construction then authorised, and to the fact that the most recent additions to the stocks of regional types had been made no more than five years previously. In 1955 it was envisaged that fifteen years on, in 1970, there would still be some 7000 steam locomotives in service.

The Modernisation Plan was presented with a good deal of publicity, and in such a way as to suggest that nothing had been done to modernise the railways for decades past. The age-old game of knocking the railways had been played long and vigorously, and in 1955 little or no credit had been given to the men of all regions, no less than those at Railway Executive headquarters, who had done so much to restore standards of mechanical performance and public service in the seven years since nationalisation. If nothing else were needed the magnificent locomotive work referred to in the previous chapter is enough to give the lie to the suggestion of no progress. When the Modernisation Plan was announced the replacement of steam traction was seized upon with avidity by all the non-technical scribes, because it was the only one of the six facets of the plan that those simple souls could understand. Colour-light signalling, automatic continuous brakes on freight trains, and mechanised marshalling yards left them all stone cold!

The factors that influenced the move to replace steam traction have already been noted, in their technical, sociological, and environmental aspects, and the leading engineers at railway headquarters in London were certainly aware, through friendly personal contacts, of the success with which diesel traction had been introduced in America. But the question was, how to tackle this huge assignment. Riddles had resigned, and the burden at headquarters rested upon R. C. Bond, who had been appointed Chief Mechanical Engineer, British Railways Central Staff, and E. S. Cox, who became his chief assistant. One of the most important questions in 1955 was to what extent diesel main line locomotives would be justified financially in British conditions, and equally how far and on which routes full electrification could be undertaken. The proposal to electrify between King's Cross and Grantham referred to earlier in this book was passed over in favour of equipping the former LMS line from Euston to Liverpool and Manchester.

Committee planning in the first place took the form of the replacement of steam in its entirety in certain areas, rather than replacement nation-wide on certain specific kinds of service. It had been shown that there would be few, if any kinds of service on which diesel traction, if properly applied, would not show an advantage in every respect over steam; by confining replacement in the first place to certain geographical areas, would have the advantage of limiting initially the capital expenditure on changes to facilities and equipment necessary for maintenance at running sheds, and workshops. While a great deal of information had been

90

gathered regarding other people's experience with diesel locomotives, the trials of the British main line diesels, only seven in
number, had not yielded uniformly good results, though they
did provide the basis on which the specifications were written
for the new main line power. Provision was made for locomotives
in three power groups initially from 800 up to 2000 horsepower,
and invitations to tender were sent out to all the British locomotive building firms. They were also sent to three firms in the
USA, one in Canada, and one in Australia.

The mere suggestion that diesel-electric locomotives might be
obtained from the USA caused alarm and indignation, all the
more so when during the Parliamentary debate on the modernisation plan Viscount Hinchingbrooke remarked that he would
have no objection to the importing of locomotives from America.
Far from being a chance remark during a Parliamentary debate,
it was learned that there was reason to believe the Commission
was seriously considering this as a means to get well-proven units
for trial in British conditions quickly. The risk was so real that it
was taken up in a strongly worded leading article in *The Engineer*:

... We feel that when they realise the full significance of such
a proposal, there will not be many Members of Parliament who
would agree with Lord Hinchingbrooke. The mere suggestion
leaves one aghast! We cannot conceive on what grounds such
a policy could be based, having regard to the great disservice
it would do to a section of British industry; but if quick delivery
is the object in view, to aid in the rapid superseding of steam
traction, then to the disservice to industry will be added much
difficulty in the running of the trains. One can quite appreciate
the desire of the Commission to implement its proposals as
soon as possible, in a spectacular manner. But we are only too
well aware of the difficulties experienced in keeping a few
closely watched diesels in service from sheds grown old in
the service of steam, and nothing would be more embarrassing
to operating staffs than to flood British Railways with foreign-

built diesel-electrics before running shed and maintenance facilities had been properly developed and the staff trained.

With the caution bred from long years of experience in providing power to run trains, Bond and his colleagues in the regions wanted time to try out the various forms of engine and transmissions, before making the vital decisions on which types to standardise; moreover there was conflict with the non-technical elements at 222 Marylebone Road, who were in such a desperate hurry to get rid of steam that it seemed unlikely that British industry could supply all the diesels needed quickly enough. Most fortunately Bond's viewpoint prevailed for a time, although the Commission received more than 200 proposals in response to its invitations to tender for diesel locomotives, with surprising variations in almost every respect, within the three power groups specified. From the mountain of paperwork involved came a recommendation to order 174 main line locomotives, which between them included seven makes of engine, eight different types of transmission, and mechanical parts from seven different locomotive builders. This diversity was a matter of deliberate policy, to provide the widest possible range of direct running experience. But what was more important was that the men of British Railways should be given time to acquire that experience.

Bond asked that following the acquisition of the new power a standstill should be imposed for about three years on the placing of further orders for diesel locomotives to give that necessary time to gain experience, and this proposal was accepted by the Commission—at first. From the delivery periods quoted it was not to be expected that the first locomotives would be in service before the end of 1957, or early in 1958, and in the meantime steam had to carry on. This was the justification for the placing of more orders for the standard locomotives *after* the Modernisation Plan had been launched. Furthermore, according to Bond's proposals no more diesel main line locomotives would be ordered until 1960–1. Even then it was expected that the transition to diesel and electric traction would be a gradual and orderly one, that would still leave some 7000 steam, of suitably selected types, in service in 1970.

There then occurred one of those curious timewasting exercises that sometimes occupy the attention of organisations in which non-technical personalities in high places have authority beyond which their experience of business generally fully justifies. Having agreed to the three-year pause requested by Bond, someone high up in the Commission bethought himself, and reasoned that if there was to be this three-year pause, what would the regions need to carry on in the meantime. It was a reasonable thought in itself, but in calling for estimates as to what would be required, it was made clear that no more steam locomotives were to be built for passenger and suburban service, and that the Commission would look with the greatest disfavour on any proposals for steam freight locomotives. As they had already agreed that no further orders for diesels should be placed for three years, and more steam was virtually banned, one indeed wonders what form of motive power was envisaged—rockets?!

It would have been laughable if the issues had not been so serious, with such an involvement of national finances, and all the time the 'scrap steam' faction was hammering away at members of the Commission, not least of its Chairman, Sir Brian Robertson. The financial position of the railways was getting steadily worse, and in the face of this those who argued that all would be well once steam was eliminated had their way. The three-year period of trial for the new diesels was abandoned, and one of the most difficult directives ever issued to a British railway mechanical engineer was issued to Bond. The introduction of diesel locomotives was to be accelerated up to the maximum rate that production capacity would allow, with two overriding provisions: first that the number of different designs of locomotive should be reduced to the absolute minimum, and secondly, that they should be thoroughly reliable and capable of

F 93

the work they were intended to do. This of course was exactly what Bond and his colleagues in the regions had in mind, when asking for the three-year testing period, but now the Commission was insisting upon the achievement of those desiderata, but denying him the time to make the necessary assessments that would ensure the most satisfactory results.

While this was primarily a problem of modernisation, and the introduction of diesel and electric traction, steam also came to be vitally affected, and, as men brought up on steam, Bond, Cox, and the regional mechanical engineers were intensely aware of impending problems that could hardly be dismissed as so many side issues. It was not just a question of deciding what designs of diesel locomotives should be manufactured in bulk, and at the speed the Commission directed. The maximum capacity of the various works, including railway shops as well as private builders was likely far to outweigh the capacity of some regions to absorb the new locomotives, either in training staff, or in arranging servicing facilities at the sheds. Diesel locomotives need clean shops for their maintenance, and to allocate them to steam depots willy nilly would be just asking for trouble. Inevitably the diesels would be allocated to first line duties when they were delivered, and viewing the situation as a whole it was equally inevitable that there would be many failures. It was no use imagining that when the diesels were delivered a similar number of steam locomotives could at once be sent to the scrap yard. It was a probability that the 'scrap steam' faction could not, or would not appreciate.

This is not to suggest that there was any back-pedalling or obstruction from the locomotive engineers on British Railways, whether at headquarters or in the regions. All realised the logical necessity for a transition from steam, and applied themselves to its problems with erudition and enthusiasm. What they deplored was the crazy way in which the programme was bulldozed into a violent acceleration. As Bond himself has written:

There were no technical reasons whatever which made it necessary to build diesel locomotives at a rate which outstripped the ability of the regions to look after them properly. The inevitable consequences were unreliable operation and general dissatisfaction all round, not to mention acrimonious arguments with contractors.

Even with the prospects of diesel-electric locomotives being delivered in far greater numbers than the original proposals formulated in 1955, there were still 359 steam locomotives to be built on authorised programmes, and there was every reason to continue design and development work to make sure that while steam remained it would continue to do the job efficiently. Any suggestion of neglect, or of running down existing power would lead to a disastrous fall in standards of train running. This might play conveniently into the hands of the 'scrap steam' faction, but it would result in serious loss of goodwill on the part of the travelling public, who were not much concerned what the form of motive power was so long as it brought the train to destination on time. In this particular period, during which the remaining 359 steam locomotives were built two important variations from standard were incorporated. The first was the Caprotti valve gear on the last thirty Class '5MT' 4-6-0s, the last steam locomotives to be built at Derby, while ten of the '9F' 2-10-0s allocated to Crewe Works were fitted with the Crosti boiler.

Interest in the Caprotti valve gear, which had always tempted locomotive engineers with prospects of higher efficiency and longer life of valves, had been revived by the excellent cylinder performance of the Class '8' Pacific No 71000, and the building of the last thirty of the '5MTs' with that gear was in keeping with inclinations at that time. Unfortunately they came upon the scene too late in the steam saga for their merits to be fully assessed, and there was general regret that circumstances did not permit one of them to be put fully through its paces on one or other of the stationary test plants. They were allocated to such sheds as Patricroft (Manchester) and Leicester (Midland), and with the principal express services from the latter then in the hands of 'Converted Royal Scots', and the occasional 'Britannia' there was little opportunity for them to show what they could do.

They had a better chance in Scotland, in the very last days of steam, when the Glasgow–Aberdeen service had been accelerated to an overall time of only three hours, and was normally being worked by Gresley 'A4' Pacifics. Some sparkling performances were noted on certain occasions when Caprotti '5MTs' were used in substitution for the bigger engines. The loads were relatively light, and to an observer in the train unaware of the type of locomotives there were times when it would have been hard to imagine an 'A4' was not on the job. One on trip, for example, engine No 73153, hauling 270 tons, averaged 83mph over the 11 level miles from Coupar Angus to Glamis with a twice repeated maximum of 88mph. Despite such exhilarating work as this, I was nevertheless interested to see that the lack of strength on the banks was also evident, even on this run.

The northbound start out of Stonehaven is heavy for the first 2·6 miles, up to milepost $227\frac{1}{2}$, and it is interesting to compare the start of the Caprotti '5MT' with those of three other runs I had personally logged at various times between 1929 and 1935, as shown in the following table.

STONEHAVEN TO MILEPOST $227\frac{1}{2}$: start-to-pass

Year	Owning railway	Engine no	Engine type	Load tons full	Time m	s
1929	LMS	14503	4-4-0*	250	5	10
1935	LNER	9509	4-4-2†	380	5	14
1935	LNER	2002	2-8-2	510	5	13
1963	BR	73153	4-6-0	270	5	18

* ex-Caledonian-Pickersgill type
† ex-NBR type

The runs of the Pickersgill 4-4-0 and of the North British Atlantic were quite normal at the period they were made, while of course the work of the second Gresley 'P2' 2-8-2 *Earl Marischal* was outstanding. It is perhaps a little unfair to take a detail from a single performance on the section from Stonehaven, but in my experience it was so typical of the Caprotti Class '5' 4-6-os as to be representative. Nevertheless experience with engines so fitted had shown that the mileage between piston and valve examination was roughly double that of engines with piston valves, and that meant they could be run from one main works repair to the next without any attention to the valves at the sheds. It was generally considered at British Railways headquarters that poppet valves would have supplanted piston valves on the larger engines, had the building of steam locomotives continued.

9 Diesel versus Steam— The Transition Begins

The first of the new main line diesels came into service in 1958, and the earliest reports of their running were coming in just at the time when I was invited to take over the authorship of the monthly 'British Locomotive Practice and Performance' feature in *The Railway Magazine* from the late Cecil J. Allen who had then just given up the feature. In the course of his amazing uninterrupted run of nearly fifty years in this particular literary chair, he had become a veritable doyen of writers on locomotive running and the recipient of a large correspondence. As the new man I inherited a great deal of this correspondence, and although in its workaday it was and still continues to be time-consuming, the aggregate of running mileage contained in the innumerable logs submitted by readers was immeasurably greater then anything I could hope to cover myself, even though I was travelling a good deal. This correspondence provided a weight of evidence, as seen by passengers clocking runs from the trains, that was invaluable in making broad assessments of locomotive capacity. To this I was able to add runs of my own, some made with the privilege of engine passes.

Before the year 1959 was out I had been able to set on record runs with the new 2000 horsepower English Electric Type '4' diesels; with the prototype 'Deltic'; with the Southern 1750hp diesels; with the Western Region diesel-hydraulics of both the

'600' and '800' classes, not to mention a 14 coach electric multiple-unit boat train on the Southern. Modernisation was definitely under way, but it was inevitable that in those early days much of the interest lay in the comparison of the efforts of the new powere with steam. As early as March 1959 I found myself writing:

I have noticed a disposition among the more ardent supporters of steam to crow over any failure of diesel power that comes to notice. While the present time can hardly be compared with the pioneer days of steam, days long before steam became a thoroughly dependable form of railway motive power, it must be conceded that a vast amount of practical running experience has to be gained in a short time with the diesels, and the failures that do occur are commendably few in the circumstances. The reactions of engine crews to such failures would provide a study in itself of footplate psychology. A driver and fireman bowling along in the comfort and cleanliness of a diesel, with an uninterrupted and unobscured view of the line ahead, could well be browned off, and discouraged from any further effort if, through no fault of their own, the diesel became a failure *en route*, and they had to carry on as best they could with the first steam locomotive that could be found for them.

Two instances when the reaction of the enginemen was just the reverse are worth recalling. On the up morning Talisman a new 2000-horsepower Type '4' diesel was provided for the Newcastle–King's Cross run. The train heating apparatus failed, and on a very cold morning the train was stopped at York and the diesel taken off. The first spare engine was a Peppercorn 'A1' Pacific, and when they restarted with this nine coach train of 325 tons, only $166\frac{3}{4}$ minutes remained for the 188·2 miles if a punctual arrival in London was to be made. The crew went for it with the utmost vigour, and despite three signal checks and two slowings for permanent way work they passed Finsbury

99

Park, 185·7 miles in 161¾ minutes. With five minutes left for the last 2½ miles a punctual arrival seemed certain, having made up 26¾ minutes of lost time; but King's Cross was not quite ready, and the train was stopped by signals at Belle Isle. On the open road there had been some very hard running, including a maximum speed of 100½mph descending from Stoke Tunnel towards Peterborough. As I remarked at the time, this was an engine performance very little below that required on the prewar Coronation streamliner, but made with a scratch engine, which the crew had taken over at a moment's notice.

This was the kind of run to delight the protagonists of steam, and equally so was an experience of my own, a little later in the transition period, when I had an engine pass to ride the Midday Scot through from Euston to Carlisle. We had one of the later batches of the Type '4' English Electric diesels, and made a good run until we were stopped by signals outside Crewe. On climbing down to telephone the power box the inspector who was riding with me noticed a considerable leak from the cooling water system and at once decided we must have a fresh engine. The locomotive was being re-manned in any case, and I met the Crewe North men who were to take us forward on the station platform. I well remember their alarm and despondency when the first spare engine available was a 'Duchess' class 4-6-2. When the guard came up the driver said, 'We'll do our best; but I'll not be held responsible if we lose a lot of time!' For my own part, riding diesels is a 'white-collar job', and I was anything but prepared to ride steam; but an overall had been found for me as quickly as they had found a substitute engine. I must admit that when I climbed aboard *Duchess of Rutland*, amid all the haste and gloom of the moment, I hardly expected that I was about to log the fastest run I had ever made from Crewe to Carlisle! It was not until the accelerations of 1970 that required use of the new Class '50' diesel-electrics in pairs that I clocked anything faster.

It was not long before our two worthies on the Midday Scot realised that they had a lovely engine, and a 'Duchess' in good trim was a joy to work. After a gentle start with this big 12-coach train of 455 tons, while they were taking the measure of her, they began to pile it on. Having passed Preston, 51 miles, in 50¾ minutes, speed was worked up to 77mph on the level before Lancaster, Carnforth, 78·3 miles, was passed in 76¾ minutes, and the 31·4 miles up to Shap Summit took no more than 35¼ minutes. By this time we had regained 8 minutes of the time lost in changing engines at Crewe, and with a brisk downhill run we passed Carlisle No 13 signal box, 139·7 miles in 138¾ minutes; but the approach and stop in Carlisle station was slow as our driver was anxious to stop the tender opposite to the water column. He needed a full tender for the hard work that would be required north of the Border. Nevertheless we stopped at Carlisle, 141 miles, in 141½ minutes from Crewe, 8½ minutes inside schedule, and a truly grand piece of work.

It can be well imagined with what enthusiasm I wrote up this experience for *The Railway Magazine* in an article in which I had paid equally warm tribute to the running of the Type '4' English Electric diesels; but I was rather startled when it eventually appeared under banner headlines, inserted by a strongly partisan sub-editor: RED DUCHESS TO THE RESCUE AT CREWE! I was worried, because all my predecessors in the authorship of 'British Locomotive Practice and Performance' had striven to maintain impartiality, and it seemed that this sub-title was crowing over a diesel failure—the kind of failure that could have happened to any form of motive power, and which was not associated with diesel power as such. Subtitles apart however it was interesting that these two instances of enginemen doing their best, when having to change horses hurriedly should have occurred with a Peppercorn 'A1' on the one hand, and a 'Duchess' on the other, because these two designs might have been put into direct competition early in British Railways' history.

When the question of the new standard steam locomotives was first under consideration, in 1950, although there was no immediate need for a standard express passenger design of Class '8' capacity, there was time for some preliminary thinking and one question was whether three or four cylinders should be adopted. Bond suggested an extended trial of the 'Duchess' class against the Peppercorn 'A1' by transferring five of the former to King's Cross shed, and five 'A1s' to Camden. The repair costs were being individually recorded under the system introduced in the 1930s on the LMS, and a comparison of coal consumptions and general performance in the regular links worked by the two sheds would, it was thought, provide valuable data for the future. Actually nothing came of this proposal so far as the two London sheds were concerned, but when E. D. Trask became Motive Power Superintendent of Scottish Region, and assumed responsibility for both the former LMS and LNER workings, an interesting series of trials was arranged within Scotland. The Night Scot was far from being the fastest of Anglo-Scottish expresses, but it was one of the heaviest, and the up train usually loaded to about 600 tons, in those immediate post-war years. Trask arranged for it to be worked successively by a 'Duchess', an 'A4' Gresley Pacific, and an 'A1' Peppercorn; but although these arrangements were known to Scottish enthusiasts, it was not an easy train to log because it did not stop in Carlisle station, but changed engines at Upperby shed. I have always understood that the visiting ex-LNER engines did adequately, but on what coal consumption and general performance I do not know.

Of course many people sought to make comparisons between the work of the new 2000 horsepower English Electric diesels, and the exisiting steam power, but it was not really a case of comparing like with like. The diesels were not likely to develop more than about 1600 horsepower at the drawbar, whereas the 'Duchesses' could sustain 2000 continuously, and touched peaks of 2500 horsepower at times. So far as the East Coast Route was concerned, in one of my earliest articles in *The Railway Magazine* I compared the running of an English Electric Type '4' on the down Talisman with that of an 'A4' Pacific on the pre-war Coronation. Both trains were loaded to 325 tons, and both passing through Peterborough at about 20mph. From there the 23·7 miles up to Stoke summit were covered in 21 minutes 41 seconds by the diesel and 19 minutes 27 seconds by the 'A4'. The maximum speeds on the level near Essendine were $77\frac{1}{2}$ and 90mph and the minima at Stoke summit $63\frac{1}{2}$ and 74mph. It was a triumph for the 'A4'—albeit nominally a much more powerful locomotive.

Critics of the diesels questioned why it should have been necessary to change over to diesel traction, when the existing steam locomotives could manifestly do so much better. It will be recalled however that the initial British experiment with main line diesel locomotives made by the LMS just *before* nationalisation envisaged the use of a pair of 1750 horsepower diesels to compete on level terms with a 'Duchess'. Thermodynamically a diesel is at its most efficient when worked at full power, and it had been felt preferable to have a stud of medium powered units that could handle the great majority of duties, and to use a pair of them in multiple for the heaviest trains. With schedules as they were during the early years of nationalisation, it was found that a single diesel could do anything needed, particularly at slow speed on heavy gradients where the available drawbar pull is so much higher than that of a steam locomotive of nominally equal tractive effort. There is a record of the second of the original LMS diesels, No 10001, taking the 9.10pm sleeping car express throughout from Euston to Glasgow, with a load of 525 tons. The climb to Shap would have been taken unassisted had not the train been stopped by signals just before Tebay; a special stop was also made to take a bank engine from Beattock up to the summit. The schedule was however very slow by later standards, providing 379 minutes for the 301·1 miles from Euston to Kingmoor No 1 Box where there was a crew change, and 141 minutes for the remaining 100·3 miles to Glasgow.

Although diesels were being ordered, there was, in the mid-

1950s, still a strong conviction that steam had an important part to play. For this reason two important exercises, one on the London Midland, and one on the Western were commenced in 1955 to improve engine performance. The first arose from the fitting of self-cleaning plates into the smokeboxes of the 'Converted Scots', which, the Motive Power Department argued, had so impaired their steaming capacity that the '7P' classification was no longer justified. Adverse comparison was made between them and the new 'Britannias'. One might have thought that with the death-knell of steam already rung, the simplest thing would have been quietly to remove the self-cleaning plates and say nothing about it. But no; the matter was referred to Rugby and engine No 46165 was put through a series of full dress trials. Some of the statements included in the official report do, however, strike one as being rather amusing, after all the praise official and otherwise heaped upon the 'Converted Scots' and emphasising how much better they were than the originals. This latter was a view to which I could never personally agree, but let that pass.

The Rugby tests of No 46165 found that the limitation in performance of the 'Converted Scots' was the size of the grate, which was considered very small in relation to the work the engines were called upon to do. It seemed rather late in the day to have discovered this, and yet this undersized grate, with an area of only 31·25sq ft if steamed to the limit on Blidworth coal, with the self-cleaning plates in, could produce 28,000lb of steam per hour, and 30,000 without the plates. This was remarkably good going, seeing that the 'Britannias' with their vastly bigger boilers and fireboxes produced only 30,250lb. There was however a tendency for the merits of the wide firebox of the Pacifics to be acclaimed, to the detriment of other types, and Rugby put forward a scheme for modifying the draughting of the 'Converted Scots' to give a 5 per cent increase in steaming capacity. To what extent this recommendation was actually implemented I cannot say; but run after run made about that time did show clearly that the 'Scots' were regularly performing work far above the level that Rugby considered their normal optimum range!

The Swindon investigation, concerned with the 'King' class engines arose in a different way. The stationary plant and dynamometer car tests of 1953, and the road trials of 1954 and 1955 with the re-draughted engines had shown that normal characteristic of ex-Great Western locomotives—a rapid falling off in the drawbar horsepower at higher speeds. Smeddle obtained authority to modify one of these engines, No 6015, by fitting a twin orifice blastpipe and double chimney, as he put it to me: '... to try and free them up'. This engine proved very free running, and with one of the testing staff from Swindon riding on the footplate a maximum speed of 108½mph was attained down the Patney–Lavington bank while working the Cornish Riviera Express. Dynamometer test runs were made in May 1956; the coal consumption for the week's running makes an interesting comparison with that of the 'Duchess' class 4-6-2 in the previous year. The loads were the same and the weather conditions calm and favourable. The results are the averages of four runs, two in each direction between Paddington and Plymouth, but with a different driver on each of four runs with both engines:

TESTS ON CORNISH RIVIERA EXPRESS

Year:	1955	1956
Engine no:	46237	6002
Engine class:	'Duchess'	'King'
Coal per dbhp hr (lb):	3·62	3·41

In view of this, authority was obtained to alter all engines of the 'King' class similarly, but the work was not completed until December 1958.

By that time the phasing out of steam had begun in earnest, except in one area, the Bournemouth and West of England lines of the Southern Region. The former was marked down for full electrification, while the West of England line, to the sorrow of all former LSWR and Southern enthusiasts was to be transferred to the Western Region. So steam had to carry on. At one time all the five main line diesel electric locomotives—the two original LMS units and the three introduced by Bulleid—were working on the Southern; the dynamometer car trials included in the Test Bulletin on the Southern diesels were conducted on the Southern Region, with the Swindon dynamometer car. This however was no more than a passing phase, and the Bournemouth expresses continued to be steam hauled right up to the time of the change to electrification, in 1967. How the trains were run in those last weeks is told in a subsequent chapter in this book. At the time of the launching of the Modernisation Plan however British Railways had to provide for steam power to cover the final ten years of this important service.

Whatever technical and operational disadvantages the third rail system of electrification has when applied to a fast-running main line, there is no doubt it can be installed with far less upheaval than the more sophisticated, and undoubtedly more efficient 25,000-volt ac system with overhead line current collection. Travellers on the Bournemouth line were spared the delays, the frustrations, the route diversions that affected the London Midland line from Euston during the time electrification work was in progress. The motive power situation on the Southern was met by the drastic rebuilding of the 'Merchant Navy' class locomotives. Nevertheless, while this gave the Southern an efficient Class '8' locomotive of its own, viewing the motive power of British Railways as a whole, and the fact that the rapid introduction of diesels would make many locomotives of Class '7' and Class '8' redundant in the near future, would it not have been better to scrap the 'Merchant Navy' class instead of indulging in an expensive rebuild, and transfer Class '7' and Class '8' engines from other regions. The 'Britannias' for example were sprinkled about the Western, London Midland, and Scottish Regions, working turn and turn about with 'Castles', 'Converted Scots' and other regional classes, and it would surely have been possible to round up sufficient of them to replace the 'Merchant Navy' class completely. This may sound like sacrilege to Southern enthusiasts, but looking at it in retrospect it would appear as better railway business.

The rebuilding of the 'Merchant Navy' class, and many of the 'West Country' class too gave us what was virtually a closely associated pair of new designs in the last years of British steam. The rebuilt engines, with an orthodox valve gear did much steady and reliable work without the eccentricities that baffled everyone who tried to secure consistent results of performance, either on a stationary plant or out on the road. One of the rebuilt engines was tested, with the Swindon dynamometer car between Waterloo and Exeter, and the results formed the basis of successful working through the last ten years of steam on the Southern, as will be told later in this book.

10 1960 and After

As the diesels began to take up their work in all Regions except the Southern, the interest, enthusiasm and industry of those who compiled logs of train running seemed to increase, rather than diminish, as the pessimists had confidently expected it would. Of course there were the diehard reactionaries, like the man who at first refused to travel in a diesel-hauled train. If a service he had selected happened to be so worked he would wait for the next, no matter how long it might be in coming! Inevitably there was a spate of comparison between diesel and steam, and because of the disparity in nominal tractive power as discussed in the previous chapter, not always to the advantage of the diesels. Fortunately however, those dedicated observers who had over the years disciplined themselves to scrupulously accurate documentation, provided much interesting evidence of the different performance characteristics of the new locomotives, compared with steam; and in respect other than straightforward nominal tractive power, one realised that it was no longer a case of comparing like for like.

Locomotive enginemen had for the first time machines on which the maintenance of power output no longer depended on the physical effort and skill of the fireman, and his powers of endurance. Noting times and speeds from the carriage an experienced observer could sense new traits in train handling,

BR STANDARDS ON DOUBLE-HEADERS

Above: Perth-London express near Lamington in the Clyde Valley climbing towards Beattock hauled by Jubilee class 4-6-0 No 45732 *Sanspareil* and BR Clan class 4-6-2 No 72007 *Clan MacIntosh*. (*Derek Cross*)

Below: A Glasgow-London car sleeper train on the G & SW line near Bowhouse with BR Class '5' 4-6-0 No 73104 piloting Gresley 'A3' Pacific No 60038 *Firdaussi* on 27 August 1962. (*Derek Cross*)

THE 'BR9' 2-10-0s AT WORK

Above: Engine No 92245 on the down Pines Express near Chilcompton on the Somerset & Dorset line. (*Ivo Peters*)

Below: Engine No 92024, with Crosti boiler on down Caledonian line freight at Greskine siding, Beattock bank, while a Liverpool-Glasgow express hauled by Stanier Class '5' 4-6-0 no 44685 overtakes it. (*Derek Cross*)

that could sometimes be rather alarming. With steam locomotives it was general practice to steam hard on the level and uphill, and then to ease off completely when it came to a downhill stretch. This was done to give the fireman a short respite, but often it was equally a matter of physical comfort on the footplate. A locomotive that was reasonably steady at 50 or 60mph could become rough or inclined to roll at 75 to 80mph especially if with easy steaming the pull on the drawbar was reduced to a fraction of its former value, and the tension, not only between the tender and the train, but between engine and tender could be lessened. Most of the diesels rode very smoothly and a driver who had time to make up would have no hesitation in allowing them to run up to the limit of the road downhill. Sometimes indeed the smoothness of the locomotive led to rather venturesome incidents, as when the driver of a 2000hp English Electric Type '4' diesel took a down West Coast express round the Penrith curves at an unchecked 77mph!

Some of the more interesting of my own observations were in my periodic journeys to and from Liverpool in 1959–60, when the English Electric diesels were beginning to take the place of steam, but before the extensive civil engineering work in preparation for electrification had begun to have so serious an effect on daily train running. There is, however, another point about the introduction of diesels on the Euston route. As it was originally hoped to have the electrification from Liverpool and Manchester complete in the early 1960s, why was it necessary to have diesels at all, as an interim stage? Surely, as on the Southern, steam could have been left to carry on until the final changeover. On the London Midland, however, there was a very important difference—the overhead wires. One of the great problems in electrifying the West Coast main line on the 25,000 volt ac system was the limitation in headroom beneath overbridges, tunnels, and other structures, and the overhead wires had to be located lower down than on railways overseas where clearances are usually greater. South of Nuneaton the clearances of the overhead wire were too tight for the larger steam loco-motives. By setting the minimum height of the wire at a lower level bridge reconstruction costs could be reduced. Moreover it was undesirable to use steam locomotives under the electric wires even with adequate clearance, because of the danger of flashovers arising from a reduction in insulation effectiveness by engine exhaust and a build up of sooty deposits on the wire and its attachments. Also, because it was expected to be several years after the completion of the Manchester and Liverpool to Euston scheme before the main line north of Weaver Junction would be electrified, there was a good case for using diesels generally, both north and south of Crewe.

The performance of the English Electric diesels in comparison to steam may be studied from runs of my own on The Mersey-side Express, to which I have added, carrying the comparison back into LNWR days, a run with one of the first 'Claughton' class 4-6-0s made in 1913. The following table is an analysis of the work between Willesden Junction and Stafford:

THE MERSEYSIDE EXPRESS

Engine Class	Load tons gross	Average speed mph	Calculated dbhp	Wt of loco tons	Dbhp per ton of loco	Dbhp per ton of TE
Claughton	435	61·7	680	116	5·85	68
Royal Scot	505	61·2	775	139½	5·55	52·5
Princess Royal	535	65·3	980	160	6·12	54·5
2000hp diesel	535	68·8	1100	133	8·28	47·2

The above figures relate to a sustained performance over a distance of 128·2 miles, and I should add that the weight of locomotive includes the tender in the case of the three steam locomotives, while so far as tractive effort is concerned, that of the steam locomotives is based upon the nominal value at 85 per cent boiler pressure, and of the diesel on the maximum value of 52,000lb.

At the time the diesels were first introduced south of Crewe the Stanier Pacifics were doing some of the finest work of their entire careers. Since nationalisation great strides had been made in restoring the track to its pre-war condition, and the loco-motives were driven hard and fast over lengthy stretches, without interruption. In the summer of 1959 I had what proved my last run with a steam locomotive on the up Red Rose, then allowed 170 minutes start-to-stop for the 158 miles from Crewe to Euston. The train was heavily loaded, with the thirteen coaches packed with passengers and providing a gross weight of 495 tons behind the tender. The engine was No 46203 *Princess Margaret Rose*. These engines, the 'Lizzies' as they were affectionately known by the men, never seemed to me quite so good or so free running as the 'Duchesses', although they had the same nominal tractive effort. They were also more arduous to fire, since they did not have the sloping grate of the 'Duchesses' and the coal had to be placed all round the box. But when capably handled they were grand engines, and 'grand' was the only word to describe the performance on that hot sultry July evening. Five times on the journey that big train was worked up to 80mph and over, and despite three signal delays and one check to 15mph for track relaying, we ran from Crewe to Euston in 159¾ minutes. If allowance is made for the four delays the net time was no more than 144 minutes, an average speed of 65¾mph.

In giving unstinted praise to these swan-song efforts with famous steam locomotives, and in the comparisons they afford to the first work of the diesels, the economics of the change must not be forgotten. When some of the English Electric Type '4s' were allocated to the North Eastern Region they began to work on the East Coast turns between Newcastle and King's Cross, and I remember that when I made my last steam run on the up Flying Scotsman, non-stop from Newcastle, with one of the 'A3s' that had been so superbly rebuilt, with optical lining up of the frames and cylinder centre lines, the corresponding down train, which we passed as usual near Tollerton, was worked by a diesel. This, however, was only the very first stage of the transition on the East Coast Route. In April 1960 I was able to set on record a run from Euston to Crewe with the prototype 'Deltic' locomotive that now reposes in the Science Museum in London. When on loan to British Railways she did much of her demonstration running on the West Coast main line, and dynamometer car trials with her were conducted over the Settle & Carlisle line.

It was with the production batch of 22 of these locomotives that the capacity for maximum utilisation of diesel power was spectacularly demonstrated. It is true that their goings and comings were very carefully regulated, and that English Electric held a contract for their maintenance, but the result showed a superiority over steam, both in performance and utilisation that I venture to suggest the most highly organised shed routines could not achieve. I shall always remember one experience of my own, after the production 'Deltics' had got fully into their stride. With a round of business appointments in the North I went down from King's Cross on the 4pm to Newcastle, 'Deltic' hauled. I stayed that night in Newcastle, and next morning had some work to do at Tyne Yard, before going on to Edinburgh. I was finished in time to catch the Flying Scotsman, which came in from London hauled by the same engine that had hauled my train down from King's Cross on the previous evening. It had gone forward to Edinburgh, returned to London during the night, and was available to work the 10am down next morning.

The allocation of Type '4' English Electric diesels to the North Eastern Region made a number of Pacifics redundant. It so happened that at about the same time there had been some alteration in the regional boundaries—tidying up the railway map as one euphemistic commentator put it—and one upshot in the West Riding of Yorkshire was that quite a slice of what had once been the Midland Railway, and afterwards LMS was transferred to the North Eastern Region. This included all lines in the Leeds area, and in consequence the big locomotive running depot at Whitehall Junction, which had housed so many famous Midland engines, came under the jurisdiction of the NE Region Motive Power Superintendent at York. One of the most important workings allocated to Leeds Midland shed was the double-home link running the service to Glasgow St Enoch, which was exclusively manned by Leeds men, and Leeds engines. The ex-G&SW men worked some turns from Glasgow to Carlisle, but not south thereof. The NE Motive Power Superintendent at that time was F. H. Petty. He was a thorough-going Gresley supporter, and thought that some of his surplus Pacifics could be profitably used on the Leeds–Glasgow double-home turns.

It is a remarkable thing that although the Midland over the Settle & Carlisle road, and the Glasgow & South Western, were such intensely proud and individualistic concerns, if one took a concensus of opinion over the years, on both sides of the Border, one would find that the favourite engines were not those of the original companies, not only in the old independent days but also in the grouping era. The Sou-West men came to prefer Midland compounds to anything they had previously driven, while south of Carlisle there came, surprisingly enough, a warm appreciation of the ex-LNWR 'Claughtons'. I remember an enthusiastic Leeds man once saying to me, 'They'd steam on bricks!' When Petty had the idea of transferring some of his surplus Pacifics the Leeds–St Enoch double-home turns were being worked mostly by 'Converted Scots', with the occasional 'Britannia'. The working of the latter engines was somewhat spasmodic, and I cannot recall ever having seen a detailed log of their working over this route. In 1960 the 'Scots', so far as the Leeds workings were concerned, seemed to have passed their prime. They were addicted to rough riding, and their steaming was not always reliable.

The Gresley 'A3' Pacifics transferred from the Newcastle area were something quite new to the men of Whitehall Junction shed, although of course they were well known and appreciated on the other side of Leeds, at Neville Hill shed. But the ex-

Midland men took to them at once, and they were soon voted the best engines they had ever worked on the Glasgow turns. I made several runs on the footplate, and saw that they were being handled in the true Gresley style with a wide open regulator and the shortest cut-off that would time the train. Quite apart from the success of these engines on the job, their regular use made the Leeds–Carlisle line unique in one respect, that at different times in its history the regular first-line express passenger power had been of Midland, LNW and then of Great Northern design. The 'A3s' ran the Glasgow double-home turns until the 'Peak' class diesels came on to the job.

As the diesels gradually took over, nearly everywhere in the country enthusiasts both individually and through the medium of one or other of the various railway societies began to realise that something they had cherished was very rapidly slipping away, and there began a rush to charter special trains to signalise the passing out of service of numerous well-loved locomotives, of the end of traditional routes as lines closed and services were rationalised, and of steam-hauled specials to mark anniversaries of famous occasions in the past history of the railways. It is good to recall that the management of British Railways responded willingly to most of these proposals, which were well organised by their promoters, and participation enjoyed in a fully responsible manner. Enthusiasm on such occasions can sometimes outstrip the bounds of safety, though incidents of this kind were notably very few. In this chapter, however, I am concerned with the changes arising in the ordinary course of railway working, rather than of special trains chartered purely for enthusiast parties.

The smaller units of the standard locomotive fleet worked unobtrusively with engines of similar power of the regional types, but one of the outstanding examples of standard locomotive utilisation as mentioned earlier was the drafting of some '9F' 2-10-0s to the Somerset & Dorset line. Until then the maximum loads normally taken without assistance over the exceptional gradients between Bath and Evercreech Junction had been eight coaches, equally by the '5MT' 4-6-0s of both LMS and BR design, and by the Southern Region 'West Country' Pacifics. This meant that a train such as the Pines Express was double-headed every weekday in the year, and on summer Saturdays, when the ordinary service was augmented by many through trains from various centres in the Midlands and the North. There was often such an acute shortage of engines at Bath that Class '3' 0-6-0 tank engines were occasionally to be seen piloting passenger trains. Use of the ex-SDJR 2-8-0 freight engines on passenger trains provided some relief, because these engines were permitted to take ten coaches unassisted; this could not be regarded as a regular expedient, and it would not in any case solve the problem of the Pines Express, which loaded to twelve coaches all the year round.

The '9F' 2-10-0s, with the much higher tractive power, and adhesion weight to match it, proved an all-time answer. They not only took twelve-coach loads with ease on the 1 in 50 gradients, but had a good turn of speed and could keep time on the more level stretches of line south of Evercreech Junction. On the Somerset & Dorset, however, it was not the diesels but railway politics that saw the end of steam, and indeed of the line itself. The first trial of a '9F' on the line had taken place in 1960, and the four engines of the class subsequently allocated remained at Bath shed and on S&D duties until the closing of the line in 1966. The Pines Express had, however, been re-routed four years earlier, to run via Southampton, Basingstoke, Reading and Oxford to reach Birmingham and its northern termini. This re-routing was one of the early steps of taking traffic away from the Somerset & Dorset line, so that the case could be made for its closure—a regrettable episode in the history of British Railways. For the record I may add that on the last run of the Pines Express over the S&D line, the locomotive was the last '9F', and the very last steam locomotive built for British Railways, No 92220 *Evening Star*.

Construction of the last batch of 'Britannias' in 1953, and

allocation of five to the Scottish Region stationed at Polmadie, Glasgow, was followed by their use on the Liverpool and Manchester Scottish trains, working through from Glasgow to Manchester. These five engines were named after Scottish firths, and they worked turn and turn about with 'Converted Scots' on these duties. As on the London–Manchester trains, and on the Irish Mails on which the work of these two engine classes could be seen side by side, to all outward appearances there seemed little to choose between them.

The preparations for electrifying the LM line from Manchester and Liverpool southward to Euston were undertaken in no half-hearted style. For one short but anxious period it was understood that no appreciable acceleration of service was contemplated after the work was finished. It was a manifestation of that strange attitude that all that was needed was electrification—'the sparks effect'—to bring back the traffic and restore the fortunes to British Railways. Happily more enterprising policies prevailed, and to provide for major acceleration and regular running at 100mph it became a case of building an entirely new railway over the tracks of the old one. A great programme of track renewal was put in hand, involving many long and severe restrictions of speed. To try and avoid too drastic deceleration of service, the principal day Anglo-Scottish expresses from London were cut to eight-coach formations, yet still run by 'Duchess' class locomotives, until there were enough of the Type '4' English Electric diesels available; sometimes, in trying to recover time lost further south some spectacular performances were put up on the heavy gradients of the North Country. On one occasion the 8-coach 'Royal Scot' was taken up the 1-in-75 gradient of Shap at a sustained 60mph. The engine was *City of Liverpool* and the load 295 tons behind the tender, and the effort involved an output of 2600 horsepower at the drawbar. It would have taken *two* English Electric type '4' diesels to match such a performance as this, though of course a single fireman would not have been able to sustain such an output for very long.

11 Anniversaries and Farewells

The idea of running anniversary specials hauled by steam loco-motives taken out of retirement goes back to 1938. In that year the blaze of railway publicity enjoyed twelve months earlier in Coronation year, with the introduction of new streamlined trains and spurts at more than 100mph, would obviously not be renewed, and the summer of 1938, particularly with the anxieties on the international front, could have been somewhat flat. How-ever, Sir Nigel Gresley was introducing new coaching stock for The Flying Scotsman, the first in Great Britain to have any form of air conditioning, and to E. G. Marsden the fact that this would coincide with the 50th anniversary of the first Race to the North, suggested a rare opportunity for publicity of an unusual kind. Marsden then held the office of Information Agent of the LNER, a post now more usually titled Public Relations Officer, and he told me how he put his idea to Gresley: if the Stirling eight-foot single No 1 were taken from York Railway Museum and put into running order, it could haul a train of 1888 period coaches, as a contrast to the new Flying Scotsman train of 1938. Marsden told how in some trepidation he put the idea forward, 'because' as he explained, 'when the Great Man is not amused, it is best to seek one's quickest line of retreat!'

Fortunately Greasley took up the idea with the utmost en-thusiasm, though the whole operation of extracting No 1 from the museum, her overhaul at Doncaster, and the selection of old Great Northern six-wheeled coaches to make up a period train was clothed in the greatest secrecy. Marsden was afraid that if the LMS got wind of what was happening they might stage a counter demonstration. They had two locomotives of the 1888 period in retirement, the ex-LNWR 2-4-0 *Hardwicke*, stored at Crewe, and the Caledonian 4-2-2 No 123, at St Rollox. Like GNR 4-2-2 No 1, *Hardwicke* was not an actual participant in the 1888 race, but the Caley single was the sole survivor of the Scottish end of the West Coast racing. The LNER sprung the surprise all right, and not until the actual day was it announced publicly that guests invited to participate in the invitation run of the new Flying Scotsman train would travel for the first part of the journey north in a period train hauled by No 1, and change to the new train at Stevenage. So intense was the interest created that a number of excursions were run later that summer using No 1 and the period train, both by the LNER itself, and also sponsored by enthusiast societies. A year later we were at war, and the germ so skilfully planted by E. G. Marsden lay dormant for many years.

It was on former LNER territory that the germ began to blossom forth after nationalisation; what better occasion for a publicity spree than the centenary of the opening of the famous Plant Works of the GNR at Doncaster, which came in 1953. An exhibition of rolling stock past and present would have been excellent in itself, but Alan F. Pegler, then a member of the board of the Eastern Region of British Railways, and a great enthusiast, conceived the idea of running special trains hauled by locomotives of Doncaster build taken out of retirement. There was no question this time of using period coaches, and as the trains were expected to prove popular and need heavy formations, it was arranged for them to be hauled by a Gresley 'A4' Pacific in one direction, and the two preserved Great Northern Atlantics in the other. As in 1938 the two retired engines, *Henry Oakley* of 1898, and the ever-famous No 251, had to be reconditioned, and where better than at Doncaster, the place of their birth. The exhibition in the Works and the special train, The Plant Centenarian, were an immense success, and enthusiasts in other parts of the country began looking forward to other anniversaries and wondering how they could be celebrated by the running of special trains.

In the very next year after the running of The Plant Centenarian, there would come the 50th anniversary of the Great Western record of records with the Ocean Mail in May 1904. What about some special runs with *City of Truro*? The idea was put to Pegler and he took it up enthusiastically, but the Western Region management was unprepared for such a revolutionary suggestion as getting one of its old engines out of York Railway Museum, and the project languished—but not for long. Although the great anniversary was let pass with scarcely a notice, the appointment of R. F. Hanks as Chairman of the Western Region Board made a great difference. Reggie Hanks, although having spent practically his whole life in a very successful career in the motor industry was a Swindon-trained man, and a life-long locomotive enthusiast. Through his interest and influence *City of Truro* was extracted from York Museum, and at Swindon she was not only put into full running order, but painted in the gorgeous pre-Churchward style, as she was when she participated so brilliantly in the running of the Ocean Mail of 9 May 1904. I have told in an earlier book *GWR Steam* (David & Charles) of some of the grand running she made on at least one special excursion in 1957; but her restoration to full running order sparked off a series of delightful events in Scotland.

James Ness was then General Manager of Scottish Region, and realising the intense value of running engines such as *City of Truro*, he authorised the restoration, to full running condition, of no fewer than four famous Scottish locomotives. Caledonian 4-2-2 No 123, and the Jones Goods—the first ever British 4-6-0—had already been preserved by the LMS, but in addition one of those splendid West Highland work-horses, a North British

'Glen' 4-4-0, and one of the very beautiful Great North of Scotland 4-4-0s were chosen for restoration to their original liveries, and in 1959 made available for working special trains. The Jones Goods 4-6-0, when first preserved, was painted green, but when reconditioned in 1959 it was given the full Stroudley yellow livery, which it is believed, but not fully confirmed, was carried on some of these engines when first delivered to the Highland Railway in 1894. These four preserved engines were used for many specials in Scotland, but particularly so in 1959 for excursions from many parts run to Glasgow for the Scottish Industries exhibition. The four engines were used in pairs, not always the same two together; to heighten interest *City of Truro* was sent north to assist in these special workings.

At that time, of course, British Railways was still fully equipped for working steam. All the regular facilities for fuelling and watering remained, and in the years 1960–3 some interesting special runs were organised taking steam locomotives, the days of which were then numbered, over unfamiliar routes. To me, some that would appear to have the greatest historical importance included the Settle & Carlisle line in their itineraries. There, in climbing the Long Drag, from Settle Junction to Blea Moor, efforts were often made to coax maximum performances out of the visiting engines. This was all the more interesting, because on that line, in the course of dynamometer car testing, some very big outputs of power had been registered. At different times the Gresley 'A4' Pacifics were incidentally pitted against the Stanier 'Duchesses', and the results were certainly impressive.

Two special runs, one with an 'A4' and one with a 'Duchess' are now compared with test results at maximum output with a 'Duchess' and with a 'Britannia'. *Mallard* was working an excursion from Alford (Lincs) to Edinburgh, via Doncaster, Leeds and Carlisle, and had a load of 365 tons, and *City of Liverpool* was on an RCTS special, loaded to 355 tons. The average speeds over the gruelling upper section of the Long Drag, from Horton to Blea Moor, were 48·8mph by *Mallard* and a thrilling 57·5mph by *City of Liverpool*. The equivalent drawbar horsepowers were 1815 and 2210 respectively. The latter was an absolutely outstanding effort. In the dynamometer car trials of *Duchess of Gloucester* the test train was made up to an equivalent of 900 tons, and in hauling it up the Long Drag at 30mph the actual output at the drawbar was 2000 horsepower. The equivalent of this on level track would have been about 2080. It required a tremendous boiler performance, with a steam rate of 38,500lb/hr, and two firemen working alternately to shovel at the rate of more than 6500lb/hr. In the six miles between Horton and Blea Moor 13 cwt of coal was fired!

At first sight it might seem that *City of Liverpool*, on the RCTS special was being worked even harder. But there was a considerable difference in the speeds, and a steam rate of 38,500lb/hr, if sustained at 55 to 60mph would probably have given a higher drawbar horsepower than 2080. Be that as it may, it is evident that *City of Liverpool* on the RCTS trips was being steamed, for a short time, very near to the utmost capacity of that great boiler. The comparison between that engine and *Mallard*, when related to the boiler proportions yields some interesting results, thus:

Engine	*No 60022* *Mallard*	*No 46247* *City of* *Liverpool*
Load, tons gross	365	355
Average speed mph		
Horton–Blea Moor	48·8	57·5
Equivalent Dbhp	1815	2210
Dbhp per sq ft of grate area	44·3	44·2
Dphp per sq ft of heating surface	0·55	0·61
Dphp per ton of nominal te	115	124

Inevitably one wishes that a Peppercorn 'A1' could have been driven up the Long Drag with comparable vigour. A 'Britannia', No 70005 *John Milton* was steamed up to 37,410lb/hr, during the Settle & Carlisle trials, and at 50mph that engine provided an equivalent drawbar horsepower of 2000 at that speed. This would have enabled a 400-ton train to have been taken up the 1-in-100 gradient at 50mph. To have sustained such an effort continuously would have needed two firemen, because the coal rate was nearly 6000lb/hr.

One of the most interesting special runs in which I participated personally was the Three Summits Tour—Aisgill; Beattock and Shap—organised by the West Riding Branch of the RCTS in June 1963, on which 'A4' and 'Duchess' class engines were used at different times. Unfortunately the 'A4' that worked the train from Leeds to Carlisle had injector trouble, and we were able to make no more than moderate speed up to Aisgill, but by way of compensation a very fast run was made from Kirkby Stephen onwards, with an average speed of exactly 80mph over the 37·6 miles from there to Cumwhinton. At Carlisle, 'A4' No 60023 *Golden Eagle*, was replaced by ex-LMS 4-6-2 No 46255 *City of Hereford*, and with our 360-ton train a fast run was made out to Beattock, 39·7 miles passed in 39min 5sec. The crew allocated to this working, however, were a youthful pair who could have had little, if any, regular top link experience in running large steam locomotives, and although this particular unit was in excellent shape, I have many times recorded much faster work out of Carlisle, in the heyday of steam. By the year 1963 steam was on its way out in earnest, although the facilities for steam running were all still available.

The Three Summits Tour train was taken across country to Auchinleck by the preserved Jones Goods 4-6-0 No 103 in all her Stroudleyesque glory, piloting a not-so-replendent Caledonian 0-6-0 goods engine, and then another 'A4', No 60004 took us down to Carlisle. There our first engine, *Golden Eagle*, was waiting to take over, with the injector trouble rectified, and her crew and inspector eager to retrieve their reputation for hard work uphill. They did indeed, and on the long 1-in-125 gradient between Clifton and Shap station a speed of 53mph was sustained—not quite up to *Mallard*'s effort on the Settle & Carlisle climb but an output of 1710 equivalent drawbar horsepower all the same. Although no further high outputs of power were involved, it was interesting to return to Leeds via the Low Gill–Ingleton line, and thence over the Little North Western from Clapham Junction to Settle Junction. The running of a Gresley Pacific over this latter section was a foretaste of present conditions, when this cross-country line to Carnforth is so frequently used by steam specials.

By 1963 we were approaching the time when it was hardly to be expected that steam specials could be run at the one-time maximum capacity of the locomotives concerned. But there were exceptions, and none more memorable than that organised by Ian Allan and H. T. S. Bailey in celebration of the 60th anniversary of the Ocean Mail record run of May 1904. This took the form of a round trip from Paddington to Plymouth and back, outward non-stop via Westbury, and returning via Bristol, and thence to Paddington by the Badminton line. It was to be an occasion of hard running throughout, and with hopes of a maximum of 100mph down Wellington bank, and perhaps at Little Somerford also, the load was kept down to no more than seven coaches. At that time the 'Castles' were being withdrawn rapidly, but there were enough left in first-class condition for a good choice to be available. Three, in specially good nick were chosen but, significant of the changing order of things on British Railways, each one was to have two firemen. Although the firing rate anticipated was not greater than anything expected of a single man in the heyday of steam, men regularly working diesels could not be expected to have that build-up of physical fitness known to the athlete that was necessary to fire a big locomotive at something like $1\frac{1}{2}$ tons of coal per hour for any length of time.

For the gross trailing load of 265 tons the chosen engines were *Pendennis Castle* from Paddington to Plymouth, *Clun Castle* (with double chimney) back to Bristol, and finally *Earl of Ducie*

125

for what was hoped to be a steam record for all time from Bristol to Paddington. It proved to be a very exciting day—though some of the incidents were not expected! *Pendennis Castle* started away in tremendous style, and in passing Patney, 81·1 miles, in 72 minutes was already 5½ minutes early on the fast schedule. Down Lavington bank 96mph had been attained when part of the grate collapsed; no one had anticipated the great heat of the specially selected coal which was too much for the firebars. It was almost like the fear that famous model engineer-author 'LBSC' once had when he rode on a little LNWR 'Precedent' class 2-4-0, and saw the fire so like an electric furnace that the fire bars might melt! Anyway, on 9 May 1964, *Pendennis Castle* had to come off at Westbury. Despite the provision of stand-by 'Castles', Westbury was not one of the places where a 'Castle' was available. Two-cylinder engine *Capel Dewi Hall* came on instead, and did well to cover the 47 miles to Taunton in 43 minutes. There a second stop was made to take on one of the 'Castles' available in case of emergency, and No 7025 *Sudeley Castle* completed the outward journey to Plymouth, covering the 82¾ miles in 97¾ minutes, practically as scheduled.

Then it was the turn of *Clun Castle*, from which some high class fireworks were expected. Inevitably there were comparisons with what had been done on the Ocean Mail sixty years earlier. By 1964 alas, *City of Truro* was no longer a working engine; and I hope the unimaginative moron who suppressed her gorgeous livery, painted her plain unlined green, and changed her number to 3717 before placing her in the museum at Swindon will hang his head in shame if he ever reads these lines! It was not to be expected that *Clun Castle* would repeat the hair-raising times that *City of Truro* made over the South Devon line, and indeed the 'Castle' was 10¾ minutes behind as early as Newton Abbot. She gained on the 'City' climbing from Exeter to Whiteball, but on Wellington bank where the Civil Engineer had ordained meticulous observance of a slack to 80mph required through Wellington station, maximum speed was 97mph. But after

STEAM SPECIALS

Above: Northbound on the Stranraer Line near Glenwhilly, hauled by Highland 4-6-0 No 103 and GNSR 4-4-0 No 49 on 15 April 1963. (*David Cross*)

Below: The Settle & Carlisle line centenary, 1 May 1976: the vintage special from Carnforth on arrival at Hellifield, hauled by ex-LNWR 2-4-0 No 790 *Hardwicke* and 4-6-2 No 4472 *Flying Scotsman*. (British Railways)

FURTHER STAGES IN TRANSITION

Above: One of the Class '40' diesel-electric locomotives (English Electric 2000 hp) on a York-Edinburgh parcels train between Cockburnspath and Innerwick. (*British Railways*)

Below: Last stage before electrification to Glasgow: a pair of Class '50' diesels on the down Midland Scot leave Carstairs for Glasgow after detaching the Edinburgh portion. (*Derek Cross*)

Bridgwater some very fast running was made along the Somerset coast line, reaching 91mph at Yatton, against *City of Truro*'s maximum of 77mph. Although *Clun Castle*'s time of $133\frac{1}{4}$ minutes for the $127\frac{1}{2}$ miles from Plymouth was 11 minutes slower than that of the Ocean Mail, it was, nevertheless, 10 minutes inside the schedule of the special of 1964.

The final stage of this truly thrilling round trip was a feast for enthusiasts on a route and service that had been diesel hauled for the last five years; but excellent though the running made by *Earl of Ducie* was, it made no records. The 'Castles' had established such a magnificent reputation in working the up Bristolian that a time of $95\frac{1}{2}$ minutes for the 117·6 miles to Paddington was little better than many of the runs I have published from time to time in *The Railway Magazine*. It would however be graceless to pass over this great effort of May 1964, undoubtedly a swansong, because it needed a great deal of organisation and planning to make such a run possible in an age when steam was disappearing fast. By the end of 1964 only eleven 'Castles' remained in traffic.

The running of steam specials became increasingly difficult, and I suppose the really classic instance came in 1968 when Alan Pegler set out to celebrate the fortieth anniversary of the inauguration of the non-stop Flying Scotsman by running his own No 4472 non-stop from King's Cross to Edinburgh. At that time of course the overriding problem was that of water. Three sets of troughs, those at Langley, Werrington Junction and Newark had been removed, and the first set out of London were then at Scrooby, 140 miles on the way. After that, the two sets on the former North Eastern main line, at Wiske Moor, and Lucker, were still in commission. The engine was fitted with an additional tender, providing an extra 6000 gallons, but to avoid extra consumption the load was limited to seven coaches, 250 tons tare behind the second tender. For comparison with normal running of 40 years previously the second tender could be taken as part of the load, which on that reckoning amounted to 330 tons gross. This would have been regarded as something very light for a Gresley Pacific in 1928, but it was a very different matter in 1968.

The long journey on which I was present began in great style on that exciting First of May. Newark 120·1 miles, was passed on time, in 125 minutes from King's Cross, and so economically had the locomotive been working that by that time the reserve supply in the second tender had not been touched. But at Scrooby troughs, where speed was reduced to 45mph to avoid wastage by splashing out, for some reason only 1000 gallons were scooped, instead of a normal 2000 at least; from that point onwards the run became one of increasing anxiety. Next we were delayed by a broken rail north of Doncaster. Had not Inspector Harland jumped down from the footplate and *run ahead*, while we were crawling up to the signal, our non-stop run would have been no more. But he obtained authority for us to pass over the fracture, at dead slow speed, and so away we went once more. The time thus lost could easily be regained, but again it became a question of how much water we would collect at Wiske Moor. We did well that time, scooping up nearly 3000 gallons, but we all held our breaths once more when adverse signals nearly stopped us at Manors, just north of Newcastle Central. Alnmouth Junction, 303·1 miles, was passed in 345¼ minutes, only 1¼ minutes late, and in the ordinary way there would have been ample in hand, with 115 minutes left in which to cover the remaining 89·6 miles to Edinburgh, though in our case much depended upon how much water was scooped at Lucker troughs.

To the consternation of us all less than 1000 gallons were picked up. In case of emergency a road tanker containing 4000 gallons of water was parked at the side of the goods line alongside Berwick station; but the last thing we wanted was to stop. Control evidently thought we should have to, and set the road for us to go through the goods loop. Worse than that, the signals were kept on until the very last moment, so that a long preliminary crawl was involved. To crown all, once we were in the goods loop the outlet signal was kept on, until by frantic signs from the footplate a message was got to the signalman at Tweedmouth Junction that we were going through. The signal was cleared just in time, but the long slowing had cost 14 minutes in running. How we regained 9 minutes between Grantshouse and Edinburgh, in a brisk and gallant finish was exhilarating, and we *did* draw into Waverley station non-stop from King's Cross. The total time was 464min 57sec to be exact, but the delays had between them cost 28 minutes, thus leaving a net time of only 437 minutes.

Three days later the train came back, also non-stop and apart from a signal check near Tollerton, which caused a few anxious moments, the train reached King's Cross in $455\frac{1}{2}$ minutes from Edinburgh. I was not able to travel on the return journey, and came south on the evening of 1 May, by the Night Scotsman, diesel hauled. Imagine my astonishment next morning to read in *The Times* of all newspapers: THIRSTY 'SCOT' STOPS TO DRINK, heading a curiously ill-informed account of the previous day's run, in which readers were told that the special train stopped *three times* to take water! From whom the Scottish correspondent of that distinguished journal gathered such rubbish it is hard to imagine; but presumably the only news of the run worth printing would be bad news, and when it did not materialise something had to be invented!

12 Requiem for British steam

Flying Scotsman came to rest in King's Cross Station on the evening of 4 May 1968. Three months later the last regular services operated by steam traction by British Railways left Preston, for Blackpool and Liverpool. At that time there were many in high places who devoutly hoped they would be really the last, and that BR would be finished with steam for good and all. For people with so little imagination it was disquieting that so many people seemed to have an interest in steam, and would apparently go to quite inordinate lengths to see it, to photograph it, and to travel behind it. That interest has far from lessened with the passing of the years, and so, ten years after that epoch-making August of 1968, it is pleasant to compose the requiem, not for something dead and gone, but for an age of which so many intensely *living* memorials exist. Furthermore, it is good to record that for British Railways steam specials can be good business, though BR does not organise their patronage. Certainly the BRB changed its policy for a total steam ban after the end of steam in 1968, to allow a limited 'return to steam' on selected specials from the early 1970s.

Ten years after the official end of steam traction on British Railways one sees its memory, its atmosphere, and its unique appeal kept alive in a variety of ways. The static museums like the transport section of the Science Museum in London, and those in Swindon and Glasgow, under the care of talented and dedicated curators, are a delight for quiet browsing, and study of old documents and pictures as well as preserved locomotives and rolling stock; but it is not in such rarefied atmospheres that the spirit of steam survives. It is in the unique aroma of a steam shed, in the living presence of an engine in steam, with its characteristic sounds and smells, which can be sensed well enough without mounting to that holy of holies—the footplate. And it is in preservation of the spirit of steam that so many activities have developed in the last ten years. Preservation of historic locomotives began many, many years before there was any thought that steam traction would one day be no more; but the preservation of sections of railway in full working order began with the little narrow gauge Talyllyn, in Central Wales, in 1950. It was a courageous effort by a group of enthusiastic and resolute amateurs—amateurs in the railway sense, but including some professional engineers—and it proved a great success. It was another matter when thoughts turned to the preservation, in working order, of branch lines marked down for closure under the Beeching axe.

Today there are a number of notably successful steam railway preservation enterprises flourishing, happily in widely separated parts of Great Britain, and all in a delightful diversity of beautiful country. One can visit them all without getting the feeling of 'just another preserved railway': Bluebell, Dart Valley, Torbay, Lakeside, North Yorkshire Moors, Severn Valley, each has its own distinctive character, and rolling stock. Then there are the splendidly organised live steam centres, from which preserved locomotives sally forth to make special runs with enthusiast-sponsored excursion trains on British Railways' metals. Didcot, nodal point of the Great Western Society's activities, Tyseley, Hereford, and Carnforth are all strong-points of the living requiem for British steam. A most important feature of all of them is that they have rail connection with sections of British Railways over which steam is still permitted to run. The locomotives preserved at these centres are therefore not captives, precluded from anything more exciting than just steaming up and down like so many caged lions.

There was a good deal of criticism when the Railway Museum at Clapham was closed, and its contents transferred to York, but in actual fact it was a masterstroke. Not only was a splendidly spacious layout made possible by using the BR steam running sheds, but the arrangements included that vital necessity for the present steam-preservation philosophy—access to a main line. At the same time, without wishing to damp the ardour or enthusiasm of those who nowadays are able to delight in steam excursions, this form of the living requiem is one that cannot last indefinitely. It is probably true to say that many of the preservationists did not realise how many parts of a steam locomotive wear out, and have to be replaced. Quite apart from such major components as boilers, many of the fittings and equipment are specialist products of numerous firms in the supply trade, of which manufacture naturally ceased with the end of steam traction on British Railways. But the very magnitude of the ultimate slaughter of steam enabled many victims not saved for preservation to have serviceable fittings removed and kept as spares to keep the favoured few going for much longer than would otherwise have been possible. A fully detailed history of many of the locomotives now in private ownership and in active service, and of their components would make some diverting reading. Like the majority of famous and long-lived engines in the full flowering of the steam age, how much of the original machines other than perhaps their frames has remained to run the million or so miles credited to them in the official statistics is questionable.

At the time of the official end of the steam age on British Railways, in August 1968, the field available for operation of steam specials was wider than it is now. Electrification of the West Coast main line north of Weaver Junction had not yet begun, and in the previous year British Railways had twice made a concession allowing steam 'under the wires' between

Crewe and Weaver Junction. This was to permit two distinguished visitors to make special runs to Carlisle. The first, in April 1967, began sensationally, in hauling the Border Limited. The engine was the famous ex-LNER 'A4' No 4498 *Sir Nigel Gresley*, worked by Crewe North men. With 385 tons behind the tender they went out of Crewe more like one of their new electrics than with an elegant museum piece. For believe it or not, in ten miles from the dead start they were doing 96mph! Checks precluded for a time a continuation of this hurricane pace, but some grand work was performed in the North Country, including a climb over the 31·4 miles from Carnforth to Shap Summit in three seconds under the level half hour.

Six months later that now familiar denizen of Tyseley, No 7029 *Clun Castle* ran the same course, on a trip organised by the Locomotive Club of Great Britain. She did not get such a clear road north of Preston as *Sir Nigel Gresley* had enjoyed, and was heavily checked for permanent way repairs between Grayrigg and Tebay. But even though the load was no more than 215 tons her acceleration to 42mph on the 1-in-75 of the Shap incline was remarkable. On that occasion the return from Carlisle was made by the Midland, also unhappily banned to steam at the present time but where, in October 1967, a very fast climb was made from Appleby to Aisgill summit. From a standing start this length of 17·5 heavily adverse miles was covered in no more than 20min 57sec, with a speed of 50mph (!) over Aisgill summit. Some strenuous efforts were made to try and get the ban upon steam lifted for the centenary day of the Settle & Carlisle line in 1976; but as any running would have ended under the wires at the northern end, such efforts proved unavailing.

The locomotives based at Didcot under the care of the Great Western Society move around from time to time, and the open days held there at the sheds are always very popular; but to see preserved Great Western steam in its most attractive and romantic setting one must travel to South Devon. The preservation of the Ashburton branch was a great achievement in itself, but that of the line from Paignton to Kingswear, part of the GWR Torbay main line, was to keep open—steam operated too—one of the most beautiful lines to be found anywhere in the Kingdom. While not having the stark grandeur of some of the Scottish mountain routes the Kingswear line in its views across Torbay, and its descent of the wooded hillside overlooking the River Dart estuary has all the more subtle and richly coloured charms of South Devon, as well as providing some worthwhile hard work for the locomotives.

It must be admitted that when preserved locomotives today are allowed to take the road, either on the short private lines, or on the prescribed routes of British Railways they are not always called upon for any very hard work. This is natural enough from the owners' point of view in striving to make their treasured, yet expendable possessions last as long as possible; but in some more professional circles there is a lingering, and quite erroneous conception that steam locomotives are more damaging to the track than diesels or electrics, and that when they are allowed on to the prescribed routes, they must be restrained in respect of maximum speed. But while a steam locomotive pounding hard up a heavy bank or doing 85 to 90mph on the level can provide a supreme thrill, it is enough to have the choice little engines of the Bluebell line in steam at all, to go steadily up the steep gradient from Keighley into the Brontë country, to see steam locomotives glide over Fowler's supremely graceful Victoria Bridge over the Severn at Arley, or to seek out the secluded Lakeside & Haverthwaite line, which to me brings back so many memories of my boyhood in the North Country.

Making the rounds of the preserved railways, and of the steam centres having connection with the British Railways network, one is ever conscious that the interests and affections of young and old alike go back not merely to British Railways steam, nor even to the Grouping Era, but to the old railway companies of 1922 and earlier; and among the major English companies there is not one that is unrepresented, somewhere, in the full glory of its original livery. It is appropriate to go to the Bluebell line to see the handsome umber style of Douglas Earle-Marsh that succeeded the exotic yellow of Stroudley on the Brighton, and two different eras of Midland painting are represented by the compound and the 4-2-2. In later years regret may be expressed that the Great Eastern and the North Eastern are not represented by more modern passenger locomotives than a Holden 2-4-0 and the 'M' class 4-4-0, however famous the latter class might be and allowing the fact that a GE '1500' 4-6-0 has been retained but in its much rebuilt form. But taken all round the North Eastern contribution is the richest of all, thanks to the enlightened policy of its management, and of the LNER in early grouping days, in keeping alive the heritage of its ancestry from the very beginning of steam railways, on the Stockton & Darlington line. Today massive ex-NER freighters pound their way over the North Yorkshire Moors line.

From the great pageant staged at Shildon in 1975, centenaries and golden jubilees have followed in succession. In 1977 the births of the *King George V* and of the *Royal Scot* have been appropriately remembered. The rescue of *King George V* from its solitary confinement at the back of the stock shed at Swindon was an epic in itself, and its restoration to full running order was another; but a further case of complete renovation grips the imagination as much for its own sake as for the precedent it could set for future exercises of the same kind. 'Precedent' is indeed the operative word! Unconsciously perhaps, those who had the idea of renovating that great little 2-4-0 *Hardwicke*, may have felt that there is a great yawning gap in the grand muster of preserved British locomotives in the absence of any representative of the greatest days of LNWR express passenger steam at Crewe. Yet recalling what a struggle it was to get the LMS of the early 1930s to save the Caley 4-2-2 No 123, the Jones Goods, and *Hardwicke* from going to the scrap heap I suppose we are lucky to have at least one LNWR passenger engine, of whatever vintage to add to the unique *Cornwall*.

The full renovation of *Hardwicke* for sesquicentennial year was a great event, while her sojourn at Carnforth in 1976, and occasional excursions along the picturesque Furness line were alike inspirations. But she had a day of even greater glory. At the end of April 1976 my wife and I went north to participate in the centenary celebrations of the Settle & Carlisle—feeling very Midland minded, and bursting with memories of school days at Giggleswick in 1916–21. But when we arrived there, late on the Friday afternoon, we learned to our horror that *both* engines that were to haul the vintage special from Carnforth next morning, and to remain at Settle on exhibition for most of the afternoon had failed! These engines were one of the two 'Black Fives' that had hauled the last steam passenger train over the line in August 1968, and the Midland compound No 1000. A massive rescue operation was in progress. The *Flying Scotsman* was being brought across from York, and to assist with the heavy vintage train *Hardwicke* was to act as pilot. The unkind thought occurred to me, how ironical it was, that engines of LNWR and Great Northern origin should have to come to the rescue of the Midland on so auspicious occasion. The purists may object that 4472 was not a Great Northern, but an LNER engine, but she was actually laid down at Doncaster before the end of 1922.

Hardwicke, and her enormous partner, can rarely have run the gauntlet of so many cine and still cameras, or registered their beats on so many tape recorders as they did that morning between Carnforth and Hellifield. To many of those onlookers, expecting the crimson rambler No 1000 to be leading the train, *Hardwicke* must have been a great surprise—and a disappointment too for the most ardent Midland partisans. But that the little engine, taken out of regular traffic as long previously as 1932, and carrying the date August 1873, was considered good enough for such an occasion was indeed a triumph for those who had been responsible for her renovation. The date she carries is actually misleading, and is that of the Ramsbottom 'Newton' class 2-4-0 which she replaced in 1892. At this latter date

138

Hardwicke was a new engine, but for all that a veteran of the first order in 1976!

Now another sesquicentenary is approaching, that of the Rainhill Trials, in 1979, and with it the news that working replicas of at least two of the participants are being built, so that the occasion may be notably celebrated. The building of such engines recalls the fascinating task set to Messrs Robert Stenson and Hawthorns Ltd fifty years ago, when Henry Ford, the American automobile magnate placed an order, not merely for a working replica, but for a *duplicate*, made of precisely the same materials and assembled in the same way as the original. Loughnan Pendred, the famous Editor of *The Engineer* at the time wrote:

> One of the pleasures of having more money than you know what to do with is that you may do things which others with a smaller coefficient of superfluity may or must not think worthwhile. America is the fortunate possessor of several such men, amongst whom is included Mr. Henry Ford.

The outcome as Pendred wrote was:

> ... It was not an easy thing to do, but it has been done, and it is possible to say, with almost absolute certainty, that the new *Rocket* is so like the first *Rocket* that its own father wouldn't know them apart.

The next *Rocket*, now being built for Rainhill 150 under the expert supervision of Michael Satow will probably not be *quite* like this, for very practical reasons; but that phrase of Pendred's 'coefficient of superfluity' stirs the imagination. There are some grievous gaps in our collection of preserved locomotives and one is tempted to ask what it might cost to build one or two of the more significant absentees anew—a broad gauge 4-2-2 perhaps? If not a Henry Ford there might be others with the requisite 'coefficient'. But here I am wandering off on sentimental grounds. How can one really avoid it, amid such a brilliant array of survivors from the death warrant of 1955. Quite a number of the preserved engines have now passed their own 100th birthdays, among them such celebrities as the Stirling eight-footer No 1 (1870), the Fletcher 2-4-0 No 910 (1872), and the Stroudley 'Terriers'. Though parts of *Cornwall* are much older, her present form dates from 1873, and then there is the doyen of them all, the Trevithick single *Columbine*. I am not forgetting all the more modern engines that have been preserved, but it was the felicitous gadding about of little *Hardwicke* that makes me remember especially the older ones.

For the present, at any rate, it looks as if modern power, and preserved steam have settled down to a peaceful co-existence, with steam operating in its own prescribed niches.

Index